AI and Computer Power

UNICOM Applied Information Technology

Each book in the series is based upon papers given at a seminar organized by UNICOM Seminars Ltd. The reports cover subjects at the forefront of information technology, and the contributors are all authorities in the subject on which they are invited to write, either as researchers or as practitioners.

1 **Fourth-Generation Systems**
   Their scope, application and methods of evaluation
   Edited by Simon Holloway

2 **Evaluating Supercomputers**
   Strategies for exploiting, evaluating and benchmarking
   Edited by A. van der Steen

3 **Failsafe Control Systems**
   Applications and emergency management
   Edited by Kevin Warwick and Ming T. Tham

4 **Computer Vision and Image Processing**
   Edited by Anthony Barrett

5 **The Distributed Development Environment**
   The art of using CASE
   Edited by Simon Holloway

6 **Software Quality and Reliability**
   Tools and methods
   Edited by Darrel Ince

7 **Open Systems for Europe**
   Edited by Tony Elliman and Colston Sanger

8 **Hypermedia/Hypertext**
   And Object-oriented Databases
   Edited by Heather Brown

9 **Software for Parallel Computers**
   Edited by R.H. Perrott

10 **Object-oriented Programming Systems**
   Tools and applications
   Edited by J.J. Florentin

11 **Object-oriented Design**
   Edited by Peter Robinson

12 **Software Reuse and Reverse Engineering in Practice**
   Edited by P.A.V. Hall

13 **Parallel Processing and Data Management**
   Edited by P. Valduriez

14 **Creating a Business-based IT strategy**
   Edited by A. Brown

15 **Executive Information Systems and Decision Support**
   Edited by Clive Holtham

16 **Information Security**
   Edited by J.E. Ettinger

17 **AI and Computer Power**
   Edited by David J. Hand

AI and Computer Power

UNICOM

APPLIED INFORMATION TECHNOLOGY 17

Edited by **David J. Hand**
Statistics Department
The Open University

CHAPMAN & HALL
London · Glasgow · New York · Tokyo · Melbourne · Madras

Published by Chapman & Hall, 2–6 Boundary Row, London SE1 8HN

Chapman & Hall, 2–6 Boundary Row, London SE1 8HN, UK

Blackie Academic & Professional, Wester Cleddens Road, Bishopbriggs, Glasgow G64 2NZ, UK

Chapman & Hall Inc., One Penn Plaza, 41st Floor, New York NY10119, USA

Chapman & Hall Japan, Thomson Publishing Japan, Hirakawacho Nemoto Building, 6F, 1-7-11 Hirakawa-cho, Chiyoda-ku, Tokyo 102, Japan

Chapman & Hall Australia, Thomas Nelson Australia, 102 Dodds Street, South Melbourne, Victoria 3205, Australia

Chapman & Hall India, R. Seshadri, 32 Second Main Road, CIT East, Madras 600 035, India

First edition 1994

© 1994 UNICOM and contributors

ISBN 0 412 45550 1

A catalogue record for this book is available from the British Library

Library of Congress Catalog Card Number available

∞ Printed on permanent acid-free text paper, manufactured in accordance with ANSI/NISO Z39.48-1992 and ANSI/NISO Z39.48-1984 (Permanence of Paper).

Printed in Great Britain at the University Press, Cambridge

Contents

List of contributors   vi

1 Statistics and computing: the promise and the risk   1
   D.J.Hand

2 AI and simulation   9
   R.J. Paul

3 Towards a statistic of metadata for knowledge analysis   23
   E. Diday

4 Simulation of uncertainty: decision support in complex
   incompletely defined environments   37
   M. von Rimscha

5 Are there any lessons to be learnt from the building of
   GLIMPSE?   53
   C.M. O'Brien

6 Handling imprecisely-known conditional probabilities   63
   S. Amarger, D. Dubois and H. Prade

7 Combining symbolic and numerical methods for reasoning
   under uncertainty   99
   P.J. Krause and J. Fox

8 Computationally intensive methods in the design of
   experiments   115
   A.C. Atkinson

9 FRIL: A support logic programming system   129
   J.F. Baldwin, T.P. Martin and B.W. Pilsworth

10 Computational models of diagnostic reasoning   149
   A. Gammerman

11 A general numerical approach to the benchmark problems
   in defeasible reasoning   169
   S.F. Roehrig

12 On the path to practical probabilistic reasoning   189
   S.O. Kimbrough and S.F. Roehrig

Contributors

M S Amarger
IRIT
Université Paul Sabatier
118 route de Narbonne
31062 Toulouse cedex
France

Professor A C Atkinson
Department of Statistical and
    Mathematical Sciences
The London School of Economics
    and Political Science
Houghton Street
London
WC2A 2AE

Professor J F Baldwin
Engineering Mathematics Department
University of Bristol
Queens Building
University Walk
Bristol BS8 1TR

Professor M A H Dempster
Department of Mathematics
University of Essex
Wivenhoe Park
Colchester CO4 3SQ

M E Diday
INRIA
University of Paris IX-Dauphine
BP105
Domaine de Voluceau
Rocqufort
78153 Le Chesney
France

M D Dubois
IRIT
Université Paul Sabatier
118 route de Narbonne
31062 Toulouse cedex
France

Dr J Fox
Biomedical Computing Unit
Imperial Cancer Research Fund
    Laboratories
PO Box 123
Lincoln's Inn Fields
London WC2A 3PX

Dr A Gammerman
Department of Computer Sciences
Herriot-Watt University
Mountbatten Building
79 Grassmarket
Edinburgh
EH1 2HT

Professor D J Hand
Statistics Department
Faculty of Mathematics
The Open University
Walton Hall
Milton Keynes
MK7 6AA

Mr Steven Kimbrough
Department of Decision Sciences
The Wharton School
University of Pennsylvania
Philadelphia
PA 19104
USA

Dr Paul J Krause
Biomedical Computing Unit
Imperial Cancer Research Fund
    Laboratories
PO Box 123
Lincoln's Inn Fields
London
WC2A 3PX

T P Martin
Engineering Mathematics Department
University of Bristol
Queens Building
University Walk
Bristol
BS8 1TR

Mr Malcolm Moore
BBN UK Limited
Software Products Division
One Heathrow Boulevard
286 Bath Road
West Drayton
Middlesex
UB7 0DQ

Dr Carl O'Brien
Statistical Computing Consultant
University of London Computer
   Centre
20 Guildford Street
London
WC1N 1DZ

Dr Ray Paul
Department of Computer Science
Brunel University
Uxbridge
Middlesex
UB8 3PH

B W Pilsworth
Engineering Mathematics Department
University of Bristol
Queens Building
University Walk
Bristol
BS8 1TR

M Henri Prade
IRIT
Université Paul Sabatier
118 route de Narbonne
31062 Toulouse cedex
France

Professor Steven F. Roehrig
School of Urban and Public Affairs
Carnegie Mellon University
Pittsburgh
PA 15213-3890
USA

Mr Michael von Rimscha
CAD CAM Concepts
Campbell House
Campbell Street
Cambridge
CB1 3NE

1 Statistics and computing: the promise and the risk

D. J. Hand
Statistics Department, The Open University

1 INTRODUCTION

The papers in this volume were selected from those presented at the UNICOM conference on 'AI and Computer Power: the Impact on Statistics', 13-14 March 1991, in London, with the addition of a few extra ones which were submitted later.

Statistics as a discipline evolves under various pressures. One is the intrinsic mathematical interest of the methods – producing the subdiscipline of mathematical statistics. Another very important one is the demand made on statistics as it moves into new application areas. This causes developments which then spread out into other areas. A glance at the past shows this effect in action: agricultural work stimulating the development of experimental design, medical work stimulating the development of survival analysis, and so on.

Yet a third pressure is illustrated by the papers in this volume: the changes that the discipline is undergoing under the impact of the immense computing power that has recently become available. And 'recent' is an appropriate term – even series of substantial conferences such as COMPSTAT and INTERFACE go back only about 20 years or so.

Even at a superficial level the extent of the interrelationship between statistics and computing is evident. For example, I understand that in most university computer centres statistical analysis makes the heaviest usage of computer time.

That phrase 'university computer centre' contains a demonstration of how computer technology is progressing, and carrying statistics with it. University computer centres are beginning to disappear, being replaced by scattered PCs and networks. Software which was once centrally controlled is now mushrooming all over the place, in increasingly powerful blooms. This dispersion has all sorts of implications for statistics as a discipline, not all of them good.

To see the range and diversity of software which is now being produced one has only to glance in recent editions of, say, *The American Statistician*. While it is gratifying to see that there is so much statistical software being produced, the range of sources does raise a real question of quality control. I am sure that each of us can relate horror stories of how some package, commercially available and widely used, gives the wrong results.

An allied problem, and one which is sometimes intertwined, is the perhaps even more common situation when the program gives the 'right' answer, but uses a formula that one would not have chosen oneself. To take a trivial example, the program might estimate variance using n as a divisor instead of (n-1). Both are correct, of course. They are merely different estimators, with different properties. This is a trivial example, and I have heard of no confusion arising from this in practice, but I have seen confusion arising in other similar situations. One can easily enough generate such situations by running a data set through different programs and comparing the results.

In fact this led me to invent an esoteric branch of science in which one conducts experiments by running different data sets through a program and tries to establish what variant of the estimating equations, what approximation to the true distribution, and so on, it uses. Sometimes this is easier than extracting the information from the producers. There is a serious point here that I would like all developers of statistical software to take note of: there should be a readily available technical manual (preferably an appendix of the command manual) which gives the formulas used, with references. This needs to be easily obtained and widely published.

The next two sections explore some ways in which increased computer power has led to considerable development of classical statistical methods and to entirely new methods of analysis. However, computers have also led to new statistics in a way which more closely parallels the effects of other disciplines referred to above. For example, the requirements of image processing have led to a growth of interest in Markov random field theory, and this is having an impact elsewhere in statistics. Similarly, work on neural networks has recently taken off, principally as a result of renewed interest following the development of the multilayer perception. These networks present a qualitatively different kind of model from those with which most statisticians are familiar.

2   CLASSICAL TECHNIQUES

Techniques in statistics which previously took days or even months to perform using hand calculation can now be undertaken effectively instantly. This in itself changes the perception of these tools and the way they are used. If it would have taken three months of calculations to fit a model then a week spent considering the appropriate form of model, using all the theoretical and substantive knowledge available was a week extremely well spent. On the other hand, if that same model could be fitted in 20 seconds, less time than it takes to make a cup of coffee (which could in any case be done concurrently!), a week spent thinking about it may be wasted – we can try 500 versions of the model before lunch!

A tool which was previously a vast, complex, and expensive piece of machinery now has the status of something we can bring into action at the wave of a hand. No wonder perceptions have changed. The danger, of course, is that thought and understanding have been replaced, at least to some extent, by brute force number-crunching power. Whether the latter can be as effective as the former remains to be seen, and I have grave doubts. Particular areas which have caused me concern are linear structural relational models applied in psychology and extremely complex multivariate anovas, with the potential for high-order interactions.

There is also a (natural) tendency not to try 500 versions of the model we originally proposed, but instead to try five models each 100 times as complicated. It seems to me that to do this effectively at least as much as 100 times as much thought should go into such models, and I am not sure that it does.

It is also generally true that the more complex the model, the more data are needed to fit it accurately. I am not sure to what extent note has been taken of this, at least in some disciplines.

Of course, I am here focusing on the negative side. The converse, positive side, is that the potential for fitting more complicated models afforded us by computer power means that we can fit more realistic models. We can relax some of the restrictions and simplifications previously necessarily imposed on us by the limitations of our calculating ability. Examples of these relaxations are the development of MANOVA and LISREL models already referred to, and others are multilevel models, random regression models, and the whole L1 norm approach, which is attracting a lot of interest, with entire conferences devoted to it.

These sort of developments in turn open up new theoretical areas. For example, the possibility of fitting more sophisticated models increases the danger of overfitting, and this in turn leads to better understanding of the problems and theoretical approaches to solving them – such as smoothing and regularisation.

This leads me on to the next consequence of increased computer power: new techniques are being developed, techniques which in some cases could not even have been dreamt of before this power became available.

3   NOVEL TECHNIQUES

Whenever one tries to identify the genesis of a scientific idea one finds that its roots arbitrarily stretch back far into the past. Clearly, the further one goes back the less similar to the current form are the ideas, so it is difficult if not impossible to say 'this started then'. Hence I am sure that every one of the techniques I am about to list was thought of in some form or other before computers became available. But without computers they were practically valueless – and so were not developed.

The list of techniques which have hinged on computer technology in this way, which would not exist without computers, is large. It includes:

1. Resampling methods, such as jackknife, bootstrap, and leaving-one-out. In some special cases, such as leaving-one-out in classical discriminant analysis, there are mathematical tricks which can alleviate the computational burden. In general, however, there are no special tricks and one will typically have to fit the model many times to different subsets of data. Many of the ideas here are extremely elegant.

2. Randomization tests, of course, have a long history, stretching at least as far back as Fisher, but they have come into their own with the advent of the computer. Many nonparametric tests are randomisation tests and use significance levels based on asymptotic approximations. Computers, producing exact values, allow us to remove any doubts about the appropriateness of these approximations, and also allow us to develop tests for more complicated situations.

3. Nonlinear problems are often analytically intractable. A computer, using iterative solutions, is essential for solving them. These sorts of techniques have permitted significant extensions in whole new areas – generalised linear models for example. The possibility of using such methods in practice in turn provides incentive for theoretical development.

4. Stochastic algorithms have blossomed under the impact of computers. Stochastic approximation was formulated in the 1950s, but required computers for worthwhile applications. Genetic algorithms and simulated annealing represent modern developments of this nature currently undergoing extensive theoretical developments.

5. Recursive partitioning algorithms for classification also became practicably feasible with the computer. Of course, here the ideas had been around for much longer, the prime example being taxonomy in biology, but then the classification trees were not typically constructed by analysing data sets but as the result of observation on cases. Automatic (and objective) recursive partitioning algorithms were developed in parallel by the statistical and AI communities, and I think the two developments illustrate nicely the difference in the two approaches. The AI researchers (who were concerned with automatic knowledge elicitation for applications such as expert systems) wanted systems that worked, and were not overly concerned with subtleties of theory. In contrast the statisticians developed precise theories and (though this does not apply in the partitioning

algorithm area) were not always concerned about small sample properties. I think this difference is manifest elsewhere in common areas of AI and statistics which have developed in parallel.

6. Other partitioning methods, such as the large number of techniques lumped together under the general heading of cluster analysis, also require computers, as do the related exploratory data analytic methods of multidimensional scaling.

7. Many of the methods mentioned above require computers because they treat the data points as individual data points, rather than trying to summarise them into some approximating model described in terms of a few parameters. Other examples of such methods are kernel and nearest neighbour discriminant analysis, which would be quite impractical without computers and are now appearing in readily available software.

8. Kernel methods are, of course, an example of smoothing techniques, and nonparametric smoothing methods, including spline methods, are currently the focus of much theoretical work.

9. Simulation is an approach to exploring properties of methods for use when the theory is difficult or intractable. Increasing numbers of papers seem to adopt a simulation approach and perhaps I can take this opportunity to remark that care is needed in conducting such a study: here the computer is certainly no substitute for careful planning and thought. In particular, to conduct an effective simulation study proper experimental design is needed, in which the various factors which might influence the outcome are identified and the range of possible influence is explored in pilot studies. As statisticians we spend enough of our time telling other scientists that they must design their studies properly; there is no excuse for us not to do so.

10. Bayesian methods, long regarded as intractable because of the computational requirements, are now becoming quite feasible thanks to the development of novel integration methods such as Gibbs sampling.

11. Other multivariate methods, such as graphical models and the use of conditional independence graphs, are also gaining in importance.

12. Finally, though this is as much an approach to a different philosophy of statistics as a 'novel technique', interactive graphics are promising to revolutionise the way statistical analysis is carried out. I shall return to this below.

4   STATISTICAL EXPERT SYSTEMS

At a meeting held in 1985, John Tukey said (Tukey, 1986) 'By 1995 or so, the largest single driving force in guiding general work on data analysis and statistics is going to be the needs that have to be met to understand and improve data-analytic expert systems.' It is 1991 at the time of writing, and I think he is going to be proved wrong. There are many other areas of statistics also undergoing intensive development, and many of them are being addressed at this meeting. However, it is also true that a considerable amount of research has been done on statistical expert systems over the last ten years.

Statistical expertise is a natural area to be addressed by developers of expert systems: statistics is ubiquitous, there are too few experts, it is as much an art as a science, and the tools of the statistician, statistical software, are widespread and widely misused. Of course, statistics was misused long before computers became available (hence such lines as 'Lies, damned lies, and statistics', which ought more properly to be directed at whoever is misusing the techniques), but computers, along with providing the scope for much greater use of statistics, also provide the scope for much greater misuse. The possibility of statistical expert systems means that, along with aggravating the problem, computers also provide the possibility of a solution.

A great many statistical expert systems have now been built. Many of these started out as small projects aimed at exploring whether or not it was feasible to build a system for the chosen domain. In most cases no clear criteria for success or failure were specified, so they succeeded, at least in part. If success meant the PhD was awarded, they succeeded. If success meant a commercially available system resulted, most did not. Only a few have reached this latter stage, and those were typically built by teams working over extended periods.

In general I think the field has matured. Now, instead of numerous small systems being built, interest is turning to more fundamental computational issues of representing statistical knowledge. Issues such as how to codify and compare statistical strategies, object-oriented representations of statistical concepts and techniques, and metadata as an intrinsic though until recently unacknowledged part of statistical data. Similarly, although assisting in preventing misapplication of statistical technique by the statistically naive was one important motivation for the initial interest in the area, it is now recognised that systems aimed at providing assistance to experts are just as valuable (and possibly more readily realised).

5   CONCLUSION

From one perspective, statistical expert systems provide an interface, not so much to statistical software as to statistical expertise. This is one kind of interface, and others have been developed. Traditionally there has been something of a distinction between statistical packages (such as SPSSX, SAS, and BMDP) and statistical languages (such as LIPSTAT, ISP, and GENSTAT). The former are usable by the less statistically sophisticated (and hence, as noted above, misusable) while, at least in some situations, the latter are less easily used. On the other hand, the latter provide ideal tools in which to develop new statistical methodology. Of course, this distinction is not a rigid one and, for example, a simple 'regress' command in one of the 'languages' is very easy to use.

In any case, other interface technologies have become important – pull-down menus, icons, mice, and so on – permitting much more straightforward and less formal interaction with the data. It is not clear to me which came first here, the relaxed interface technology or relaxed styles of data analysis emphasising graphical displays and informal exploration. Perhaps, like chickens and eggs, from the viewpoint of statistics they came together. In any case, it is quite striking how different is the approach to data analysis with an emphasis on informal data examination from more formal model-building approaches. The difference in philosophy is not of a kind with the Bayesian/frequentist distinction, but it is just as deep and just as significant.

Most of the discussion above has addressed the topic of this meeting through the direct impact of computers and AI on statistics. But they have a more subtle influence by introducing scientific problems for which new statistical methods are needed. An important example is the applications statistical theory within expert systems. Expert systems often deal with inference on uncertain data, and statistics is, after all, the science of uncertainty management.

Several formalisms other than probability have been proposed for handling uncertainty in expert systems. This is because some researchers feel that there are different kinds of uncertainty involved and that probability is not appropriate for handling all of them. However, probability has the advantage of extensive theoretical development going back over centuries (even if the axioms were only formalised in the 1930s). Recent developments in computation with probabilities on graphical structures have demonstrated that probability can solve many of the problems of uncertainty inference in expert systems.

Obviously in this short paper I cannot cover everything, and there are many areas of the interaction between statistics and AI and computers that I have not covered: complex econometric models, software and hardware reliability, information retrieval, statistical databases, to name but four. However, there is one area which it would be remiss not to mention. This is statistical education.

The advent of the computer has opened up a whole new world of possibilities for those concerned with teaching statistics. In the past the essence of a statistical education has lain in acquiring the ability to perform the numerical calculations. The whys and wherefores, the diagnostics, notions of how to match the researcher's question, were left until the students graduated, and found themselves confronted by the messiness of real problems. Now this is no longer necessary, or even acceptable. Now the computer will do the arithmetic. Indeed, now it is unnecessary for most users of statistics to know the algebraic form of (say) a least-squares solution. What those users must know, however, is what regression coefficients mean, how to choose between using simple and multiple regression, and how to interpret the various diagnostic plots. Since the computer will automatically do the arithmetic the time which formerly was spent teaching arithmetic and algebraic details can now be spent on these more fundamental and important topics.

And I have said nothing about the educational possibilities opened up by the scope for running imaginary experiments, for simulating data, for doing laboratory work in class in minutes which would previously have taken hours, or of the possibilities opened up by computer-assisted learning.

To summarise, the computer is freeing users of statistics from the tedium. It is allowing them to concentrate on the challenging higher level problems. Computers and AI are changing the face of statistics. The papers which follow illustrate some of the ways in which this is happening.

REFERENCE

Tukey, J.W. (1986) An alphabet for statistician's expert systems. In W. A. Gale, AI and Statistics, Reading, Massachusetts: Addison-Wesley.

2 AI and simulation

R. J. Paul
Brunel University

1 INTRODUCTION

Simulation modelling research started for the CASM Research Group in 1982. A great variety of research has been undertaken since then, and has been widely reported. The basic objectives of the research group are to make the process of simulation modelling more effective and efficient by the production of software-based systems. These systems are designed to automate those aspects of the simulation modelling process that are relatively straight-forward, tedious and time consuming to undertake. For example the generation of a simulation program has been extensively automated in several CASM applications (see Paul and Chew 1987, Knox 1988, and Au 1990). Figure 1 illustrates the basic idea behind the automation of the modelling process as envisaged by large parts of the CASM research endeavour. The objective is to allow the analyst and the customer to work together to formulate the problem that is being modelled, using software systems that allow fast and effective interaction. Such systems, it is anticipated, will be graphics based, and sections 3 and 4 of this paper describes some work that has led to the production of a graphics driven simulation environment. When the model to be simulated is understood by the system, then there are a number of alternative ways of proceeding. The one which CASM has most commonly used is that of automatic program generation, and these generators are also described in section 4.

Section 5 looks at an expert system that has been developed to assist in correcting simulation programs. The use of semantic analysis in a system that incorporates procedural attachment is recounted in section 6. Section 7 examines some statistical issues in output analysis, explaining the surprising lack of AI support in this area. First, we outline the simulation context within which the work in this paper functions.

2 DISCRETE EVENT SIMULATION MODELLING

Simulation is a set of techniques for using a computer to imitate the operations of various kinds of real-world facilities or processes. It is typically used to study models of real-world problems that are too complex to be evaluated analytically. In order to study scientifically the facility or process of interest, a set of assumptions about how it works has to be made. These assumptions, which usually take the form of mathematical or logical relationships, constitute a model which is used to try and gain some understanding of how the corresponding system behaves.

A computer is used to evaluate the model numerically over a time period of interest to estimate the desired true characteristics of the model. For example, a port which handles a variety of incoming and outgoing cargoes, using a mixture of specialised and general berths, has been simulated in order to aid the planning of future berth requirements (El Sheikh et al., 1987). The simulation model was used to simulate the operation of the port as it currently exists and as it would be if the port were expanded or not. Holder and Gittins (1989) report on the effect of warship and replenishment ship attrition on war arsenal requirements. A group of such ships is simulated over extended periods of time in order to determine ship weapon usage. The model is used to study the impact of attrition, including the effects of preferential targeting, and the correlation between the usages of different weapon systems, on war arsenal requirements.

Simulation, then, involves the setting up of a model of the system under study, in which all the relevant components are defined, and the ways in which they change through time and affect each other are exactly specified. Typically the simulation model is stochastic because it will contain several random variables (for example, the inter-arrival times of ships at a port may be random). The model is set in motion and its behaviour observed. The output data for a stochastic process simulation model are themselves random and thus are only estimates of the true characteristics of the model. If the model is of an actual system, then the model can be run for a set time, and the value taken by the output variables can be compared to the values taken by the corresponding variables in the real system. If the correspondence is close, then the model may be considered to be a good representation of reality. The model then provides a potentially powerful tool for conducting controlled experiments, by systematically varying specific parameters and re-running the model. Simulation models of hypothetical systems can similarly be experimented with, albeit with more caution.

The survey conducted by Beasley and Whitchurch (1984) provides evidence that simulation is an important modelling technique. However, simulation is expensive to use in spite of recent advances in computing hardware and software. The survey by Christy and Watson (1983) shows that the cost of simulation using current software systems is still one of the major disadvantages of using simulation modelling. What is clear from both papers is that simulation modelling is a powerful method for modelling problems and it would be more widely used if it became cheaper and easier to do so.

The practice of simulation has grown in parallel with the development of computing power. Simulation modellers were quick to recognise the benefits of specialised simulation structures to promote the efficient construction and testing of large models. More recently, program generators have further speeded up the process of model coding. Microcomputers have allowed the modeller literally to take the model rather than simply a mass of computer output to the user for verification. Computer graphics have also been used to improve the end-user acceptability of simulation models and their results.

However, simulation remains an expensive technique. Greater processing power has encouraged the wider use of simulation rather than possible analytic alternatives. More ambitious models encompass ever greater volumes of detail. The relative expense of simulation is now largely a function of analyst rather than computer time and the pressure to improve the productivity of the analyst increases and will continue to do so.

3   SIMULATION PROBLEM FORMULATION

A number of applications involving aspects of artificial intelligence have already been developed within the CASM group. Paul and Doukidis (1986) have reported on their natural understanding system that allows the customer and the analyst to specify the simulation problem using a natural language interface. This basically follows the logic of an activity cycle diagram without making this explicit. The natural language understanding system produces a text file of the basic simulation problem logic, which can be fed into a simulation ISPG to produce a working Pascal program.

Whilst the system actually worked in a research sense, it was not turned into a production system because of its limitation which was appreciated at this stage. Natural language via a computer terminal is not a natural method of communication between two people, i.e. the customer and the analyst. The entry of structured sentences, and the analysis of such sentences by the computer system, would try and test the patience of the customer beyond endurance. Another feature of such an approach is that it does not provide for a visual simulation construction, which is nowadays becoming de rigueur for any simulation package. However, there were a number of benefits of this research, and it is hoped to incorporate some of the ideas that were gleaned in these efforts in the creation of a richer graphics driven environment.

Abdurahiman and Paul (1992) report on the use of machine learning in simulation model formulation. Machine learning plays a central role in artificial intelligence. The study and computer modelling of learning processes in their multiple manifestations constitutes the subject matter of machine learning. Several of our intuitive ideas about the nature of human learning are equally valid in describing machine learning. Learning can be generally classified as either enhancing skills of the learner or in acquiring knowledge for the learner. The first kind is a gradual improvement of motor and cognitive skills through practice, where as the second kind involves the collection, classification, organisation, integration, and abstraction of knowledge. It has been demonstrated that the learning strategy is a function of knowledge and an important parameter in the classification of learning strategies is the degree of inference required on the part of the learner (system). At one extreme the learner uses no inference but directly accepts and uses the information given to him. At the other extreme, the learner performs a very substantial amount of inference which sometimes leads to discovery of new knowledge.

The proposed system would use the 'learning from example' strategy to learn the system behaviour under study. Learning from examples is also called inductive learning which is the most researched strategy in artificial intelligence. The analyst could give examples of the system through an interface; the system thus would induce the description of the system (hypothesis) from examples provided by the analyst. The method we shall use is the multi-step process in which examples are provided one by one to the system. In order for the system to induce such a description, it needs an additional knowledge base to constrain the possibilities and guide the inference process towards one or a few plausible hypotheses.

4   GRAPHICS DRIVEN ENVIRONMENTS

The Computer Aided Simulation Modelling (CASM) project is researching into ways of automating parts of the process of simulation modelling. Full details of the CASM research are given in Balmer and Paul (1986) and Paul (1990). The CASM project team has been working on a flexible plan for developing computer aids for simulation modelling. Here an overview of this plan is given in order to illustrate the potential areas of application for expert systems.

Figure 1 illustrates the basic process of simulation model development as envisaged by Balmer and Paul (1986). The analyst, after consulting the decision maker(s) or client(s), formulates the problem in some structured way, for example as an activity cycle diagram (ACD) or a flowchart. ACDs are described by Clementson (1982) and Szymankiewicz et al. (1988) among others. The model logic thus defined is fed into an interactive simulation program generator (ISPG). Several ISPGs exist, such as CAPS by Clementson (1982), AUTOSIM, a Pascal emulation of CAPS by Paul and Chew (1987), and VS6 described by Knox (1988) and Paul (1990). These ISPGs interactively determine the characteristics of the problem ACD, including quantitative information concerning sampling, arithmetic and initial conditions. The program generator then automatically writes the simulation model using a host of software subsystems. These latter would include a model structure (in our case, the three-phase method – see Pidd (1992) for a description of this method) and various routines for data sampling, queue manipulation, recording etc. For example, AUTOSIM accesses the LIBSIM software subsystem to produce the simulation program. LIBSIM is described by Crookes et al. (1986) and Paul and Chew (1987). Under control of the analyst, the model is run and output is produced. The output can be used to determine the 'correctness' of the model logic and of the computer program, as well as providing guidance to the experimental results required.

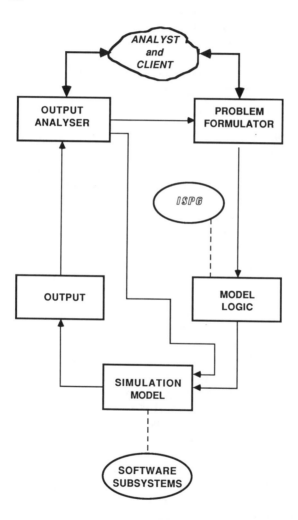

Figure 1   The process of simulation modelling.

Assuming that the above process works satisfactorily, the labour intensive activities remaining are problem formulation and output analysis (plus client satisfaction!). These activities are 'intelligent' contributions of an analyst which tend to improve with experience. In Figure 1, problem formulation is depicted with the aid of an AI system which helps the analyst formulate the problem with the customer. The expertise of the analyst can similarly be further captured in an output analyser to help decide what if anything is wrong and how to run the model to obtain satisfactory answers. The modelling environment more closely represents practical as well as desirable model development. The simulation environment is not depicted as a single-pass system, but as a continuous loop of activity. This enables gradual model development in small, easily checked stages, model correction in the light of program output, and determination of the running conditions and run lengths of the simulation model. The latter could be determined dynamically as a function of output and hence the feedback loop from the output analyser to the simulation model. The analyst is in control of, and participates in, this process. A major benefit of rapid model development is that the client can participate in the modelling process as well. In these ways, integration of the system is advanced considerably.

The latest development in these environments is described by Au (1990) and Au and Paul (1992). This graphics driven environment allows the users, the analyst and the customer to specify the problem using iconic representations for the objects in the system. The icons are laid out on the screen in a logical fashion, intelligible to the user as well as to the analyst. No particular formulism is used for this, in terms of diagrams or methods, although underpinning the method is the activity cycle diagram concept. This system was developed on the Macintosh microcomputer, which is an ideal environment for mixing graphics display with text. The system provides the user with assistance in the construction of the logic of the problem, and in the addition of quantitative and conditional information to the model logic.

A feature of this system is that different levels of detail concerning the problem are constructed in parallel by a mixture of diagramming methods and tabular information. So, for example, if the users specify an object such as a person in the system, then this person can be represented by an easily identifiable icon. At the same time, a description of what type of object or entity a person is can be input to a table. The MacGRaSE system allows the user to draw the equivalent activity cycle diagram for the problem. The problem can be run in interpretive mode so that the dynamics of the system can be seen on the screen, checked and verified as much as any such visual representation can verify anything. Some complex simulations might be difficult if not impossible to describe completely using such a graphics driven specification environment. MacGRaSE allows a more basic model to be input and generated as a Pascal program, so that the particular idiosyncratic difficulties can be edited in to the program code. Such complexities usually revolve around the conditions for an activity to start, and often involve several levels of conditional statement, which is difficult to encompass entirely within a graphics driven environment.

Future work in this area is intended to remedy some of the possible deficiencies in complexity of problem that can be handled by this system. This might be achieved using a mixture of graphics and artificial intelligence techniques. Further enhancements might in any case be provided by producing a richer mixture of interrelated screens for the analyst to specify the problem with, plus some better help facilities for reminding the user of what is required for a complete specification. Hopefully, in the not too distant future, one might build such an environment and incorporate the benefits of the research in formal methods described by Domingo and Paul (1992).

5   SIMULATION PROGRAMMING DEBUGGING

As mentioned above, at the heart of the CASM simulation system depicted in Figure 1 is a suite of Pascal routines that provide the support for writing discrete event simulation programs using the three-phase simulation structure (Crookes et al., 1986). This system is supported by an interactive simulation program generator (ISPG) that, based on information taken from an ACD description of the problem, produces a Pascal simulation program using the suite of supporting routines (Paul and Chew, 1987). Powerful though this type of ISPG is, some complex problem decision rules cannot always be handled directly, requiring the amendment of the generated code. Also, re-evaluation of the problem being modelled gives the analyst the choice of using the ISPG again or amending the code.

A variety of amended program errors, both run-time and in the output, have been determined from experience of teaching students and of applied work with the systems. These errors are typically diagnosed by a limited number of 'experts' in the simulation system, and whose availability is usually restricted. A number of solutions to this problem of scarcity of expert advice have been devised, and the expert system debugger SIPDES (SImulation Program Debugger using an Expert System) described by Doukidis and Paul (1991) is one of them.

SIPDES is designed to help an analyst discover where his simulation program written with the CASM systems has gone wrong. The error may be a run-time error (for example, attempting to move an entity from an empty queue) or it may be an obvious mistake in the output (for example, nothing happened, or an entity disappears completely over time). The SIPDES system provides messages to facilitate the nature of the hypothesis being tested as well as the normal help facilities. SIPDES was developed as a debugging tool for the following reasons. The problem of debugging simulation program code has all the hallmarks of an expert system. The availability of an expert system development environment made the task of writing SIPDES feasible. Crucially, the CASM software systems are under constant development. Whilst the systems could be updated for potential user mistakes, these are difficult to determine before the system modifications have been made. Empirical evidence is required to determine new problems that arise. Only run-time errors can be detected within the system. Mistakes that can only be detected at the reporting stage cannot be determined by an inbuilt error system.

With the development of the CASM systems, the incorporation of run-time error detection expands disproportionately with the size of the system, consuming more computer memory and/or slowing the system down. Since an ISPG program will work, and efficiency is a major objective, the incorporation of an expensive and frequently updated run-time error detecting system into the simulation system is an expensive aberration. Run-time errors should be few if the systems are used correctly and can readily be sought from the expert system. The latter can also aid the determination of mistakes detected at the report stage.

SIPDES is not a purely diagnostic expert system. It includes detailed step-by-step instructions for trouble-shooting when the cause of the problem cannot be identified precisely. It is intended to serve both as a training tool and as a debugging aid for inexperienced (and sometimes experienced) CASM users. When a hypothesis has been proved, a course of action is recommended to the user. When it is appropriate, the system provides extra information on what that action may entail, after giving examples of the correct code required.

When SIPDES is run, the user is presented with a top-level set of goals, as shown below:

> At which stage was the error noted?
> 1   Before all Bound-Events had been completed at least once.
> 2   Sometime in the simulation run.
> 3   At the simulation final REPORT.

The user, by choosing any of these options, can narrow the search by indicating the subgoal to focus on. Once the specific rules are evoked, SIPDES works as a regular back-chainer.

SIPDES can explain its line of reasoning at any point on demand. It uses both the general explanation facility provided by the skeletal expert system ASPES (Doukidis and Paul, 1987) and one specially designed for this domain.

Hill and Roberts (1987) have similarly developed a prototype knowledge-based support system. It mimics the diagnostic process that teachers using the simulation package INSIGHT give students. The system is written in Prolog. Unlike SIPDES, the knowledge base contains knowledge concerning the assignments given to students. This should enable it to give more exact advice, whilst being restricted in its application. The authors describe a range of extensions they envisage, along with some words of caution as to the viability of all that may appear desirable!

Moser (1986) sees decision support systems, where artificial intelligence aids the decision maker in interpreting simulation output, as an area of potential. He has developed a simple system to demonstrate the idea. The problem simulated is that of financial investment decisions, with the expert system interpreting the output from the simulation run for the decision maker. The system allows the decision maker to interrogate the results for a variety of possible outcomes.

Spiegel and LaVallee (1988) report on the use of an expert system to drive a simulation. The expert system is provided with a number of rules which describe, qualitatively, how various simulation parameters effect specific simulation results. The expert system is used to monitor simulation statistics and control simulation parameters.

Knowledge acquisition in developing SIPDES was found to be one of the most difficult tasks. Top-down division of the problem into a knowledge-tree was used. The construction of the knowledge-tree proved invaluable. It gave at a glance the number of errors acquired, their causes, and any patterns that existed. A major proportion of the system development time was spent on the acquisition and development of the knowledge base to an acceptable level.

The system has several advantages over, say, a dictionary of symptoms of errors. It is readily expandable both in width (new areas of problems) and in depth (symptoms associated with an error). SIPDES is a guide that will help the user systematically through his program. This dynamic interactive characteristic is the system's most important quality. Running the simulation program itself within the debugging system to determine which hypothesis is correct is a longer-term research objective.

6   SEMANTIC ANALYSIS

Another research direction, which incorporates many aspects of artificial intelligence, is a simulation system which is very different to those described above. This simulation system is based on a spreadsheet approach to simulation software. This approach was adopted since it was felt that many potential users of simulation modelling are already familiar with spreadsheet packages such as Lotus 1-2-3. So the interface to this package is basically similar to Lotus 1-2-3 itself. A description of the simulation problem can be written in natural language form, and then the simulation system will interpret this natural language using some artificial intelligence approaches such as semantic networks. So one spreadsheet level in the simulation package, as described by Barakat (1992), is a semantic network connecting the objects in the system to their definition, such as entities, activities and so on. A second equivalent level to this, in spreadsheet terms, provides an activity cycle diagram for the problem. A third equivalent level in the spreadsheet system provides the numerical data required to actually run the simulation model. It is also possible to add to the system an iconic visual representation which can be run dynamically.

Apart from semantic networks, other aspects of artificial intelligence incorporated in this system include an expert system that allows a user to uncover the connections between any part of the system and any other part. The expert system uses the semantic network to trace through the connections, and to provide a full description of the connections between the two specified objects.

Rather than using a simulation program generator approach, this system allows itself to be reconfigured if the problem to be modelled cannot be handled by the system as it is currently built. The architecture of the system allows the analyst to add new constructs to the simulation architecture. These constructs typically concern the complexity of conditions for beginning an activity. So the user may write a new set of conditional types in Pascal for the particular problem. These can be incorporated into the system, which can then be recompiled into a complete data-driven system as before. This method of approach, known as procedural attachment in artificial intelligence, adds a different and potentially exciting opportunity to all the simulation systems being researched into by CASM.

7   EXPERIMENTAL DESIGN AND OUTPUT ANALYSIS

Problem solving using discrete event simulation modelling is usually a statistical experiment. The analyst is attempting to obtain meaningful answers from a random process as efficiently as possible. There is an extensive statistical literature, including specialist work on simulation (for example, see Law and Kelton, 1991). Part of the CASM objectives outlined above includes incorporating this knowledge in an output analyser to assist the analyst with the experiment (see Figure 1). However, work in this area is difficult for reasons that are now explained.

A single simulation run of somewhat arbitrary length will provide simulation estimates which might erroneously be considered as the correct answers for the model. Since these estimates are random variables which may have large variances, they could differ greatly from the corresponding true answers. One reason for the historical lack of definitive data analysis is that simulation output data are rarely independent. Classical statistical analyses based on independent identically distributed observations are not directly applicable. A further difficulty in obtaining accurate estimates of a model's outputs is the computer cost of collecting the necessary amount of simulation output data.

Another complication is that there are two types of simulation with regard to analysis of output. A terminating simulation is one in which the desired measures of system performance are defined relative to when some specific event occurs. For example, a battle is completed when one side withdraws or is defeated (see Holder and Gittins, 1989). In this case, the simulated time can often be a random variable. A steady-state simulation is one for which the measures of performance are defined as the length of the simulation goes to infinity (as for example in the port described by El Sheikh et al., 1987). Hence the length of the simulation run must be long enough to get good estimates of the quantities of interest. The difficulty with steady-state simulation is recognising when the simulation has arrived in the steady-state. Leading output variables of interest can be calculated at regular intervals of time to detect when the average of these draws to a limit. Automation of this approach has to avoid the danger of excessive run times.

To handle stochastic output, an obvious need is for confidence intervals on the variables of interest. One method is to use a fixed sample size approach. However, the analyst then has no control after the sample size has been selected. Law and Kelton (1991) describe various methods for obtaining confidence intervals with specified precision. Among these are sequential procedures by which the length of the simulation is sequentially increased until an acceptable confidence interval can be constructed using one of several techniques for stopping the simulation run. Similar observations can be made when using a simulation model to compare alternative systems. Many methods have been proposed to achieve such comparisons, but the definitive solution has not yet been given.

Variance reduction techniques are a method of conducting a simulation experiment where the confidence in the model is balanced against the cost of obtaining the solutions. Efficient methods of obtaining desired levels of confidence enable tighter levels of confidence to be sought at the same cost. Many methods for achieving these ends include common random number streams, antithetic variates, control variates, indirect estimation, and the use of conditional expectations where appropriate. These methods do not consistently provide the expected benefits that have been claimed on the basis of simple modelling experiments, when they are applied to complex problems. For example, it is not clear how to even apply the oft-mentioned antithetic variate method to models with several input variables.

Some simulation experiments deal with problems where the structure of the goal of the study is less evident. In this context, experimental design provides a way of deciding beforehand which particular system variants to simulate so that the desired information can be obtained at minimal cost.

Carefully thought-out experiments are much more efficient than a hit-or-miss sequence of runs which simply try a number of systems unsystematically to see what happens. Factorial designs and fractional factorial designs are particularly useful in the early stages of experimentation when seeking the factors which are important and how they might affect the response. A whole variety of techniques known as response-surface methodologies can be used, as more is understood about the behaviour of the model, to find the optimal combination of factor specifications. Automation at this level of sophistication has not yet emerged.

Taylor and Hurrion (1988) and Taylor (1988) report on an expert advisor for simulation experimental design and analysis. The work clearly demonstrates the feasibility of such systems. Users define the objectives of their study (with default values as alternatives). The system gathers information about the problem under consideration. An initial experiment is devised using production rules according to the objectives of the study. The analysis of the results of the first experiment may prompt the advisory system to refine the experiment or request further experiments before it can yield a sensible conclusion. The system demonstrates that such a framework for an advisor is robust. Taylor (1988) describes some of the future research that he concludes is required, for example in model testing and evaluation.

Clearly the statistical aspects of simulation modelling can be formidable. Coming at the end of the modelling process, there is a great temptation to use the model optimistically under time and resource constraint pressure. Whilst all of the statistical aspects of the process have not been solved, there is a body of available expertise. Hence in Figure 1 an intelligent output analyser under the guidance of the analyst is seen as a desirable if not necessary component of a simulation modelling environment. The opportunity for applied expert systems and statistical research in this area is extensive.

REFERENCES

Abdurahiman, V. and Paul, R.J. (1992) Machine learning and simulation model specification. Submitted to European Journal of Operational Research.

Au, G. (1990) A Graphics Driven Approach to Discrete Event Simulation Models. Unpublished PhD thesis. University of London.

Au, G. and Paul, R.J. (1992) A Graphical Discrete-Event Simulation Environment. Submitted to Journal of the Operational Research Society.

Balmer, D.W. and Paul, R.J. (1986) CASM – The right environment for simulation. Journal of the Operational Research Society 37, 443–452.

Barakat, M. (1992) Semantic Modelling for Discrete Event Simulation. Unpublished PhD thesis. University of London.

Beasley, J.E. and Whitchurch, G. (1984) O.R. education – a survey of young O.R. workers. Journal of the Operational Research Society 35, 281–288.

Christy, D.P. and Watson, H.J. (1983) The application of simulation: a survey of industry practice. Interfaces, 13, 47–52.

Clementson, A.T. (1982) Extended Control and Simulation Language. Cle. Com Ltd., Birmingham, UK.

Crookes, J.G., Balmer, D.W., Chew, S.T. and Paul, R.J. (1986) A three phase simulation system written in Pascal. Journal of the Operational Research Society, 37, 603–618.

Domingo, L.T. and R.J.Paul (1992) An Introduction to Simulation Specification Using Formal Methods. Submitted to the Journal of the Operational Research Society.

Doukidis, G.I. and Paul, R.J. (1987) ASPES – a skeletal Pascal expert system, In Expert Systems and Artificial Intelligence, in Decision Support Systems (eds. H.G.Sol et al.), D. Reidel, Dordrecht, Holland. pp. 227–246.

Doukidis, G.I. and Paul, R.J. (1991) 'SIPDES: A Simulation Program Debugger Using an Expert System' accepted by Expert Systems With Applications, Vol. 2.

Sheikh, A.A.R. El, Paul, R.J., Harding, A.S. and Balmer, D.W. (1987) A microcomputer based simulation study of a port. Journal of the Operational Research Society, 37, 673–681.

Hill, T.R. and Roberts, S.D. (1987) A prototype knowledge-based simulation support system. Simulation, 48, 152–161.

Holder, R.D. and Gittins, R.P. (1989) The effects of warship and replenishment attrition on war arsenal requirements. Journal of the Operational Research Society, 40, 167–175.

Knox, P.M. (1988) Automated Graphically-Based Discrete-Event Simulation Systems. Unpublished PhD thesis. University of London.

Law, A.M. and Kelton, W.D. (1991) Simulation Modeling and Analysis. 2nd edition. McGraw-Hill, New York.

Moser, J.G. (1986) Integration of artificial intelligence and simulation in a comprehensive decision-support system. Simulation, 47, 223–229.

Paul, R.J. (1990) Simulation Modelling: The CASM Project. Journal of the Brazilian Operations Research Society, 10:2, 1–34.

Paul, R.J. and Chew, S.T. (1987) Simulation Modelling using an Interactive Simulation Program Generator. Journal of the Operational Society, 38, 735–752.

Paul, R.J. and Doukidis, G.I. (1986) Further developments in the use of artificial intelligence to formulate simulation problems. Journal of the Operational Research Society, 37, 787–810.

Pidd, M. (1992) Computer Simulation in Management Science. 3rd edition. Wiley, Chichester.

Spiegel, J.R. and LaVallee, D.B. (1988) Using an expert system to drive a simulation experiment, in AI Papers, 1988 (R.J. Uttamsingh, Ed.), Simulation Series Vol. 20, No. 1, The Society for Computer Simulation, San Diego.

Szymankiewicz, J., McDonald, J. and Turner, K. (1988) Solving Business Problems by Simulation. McGraw-Hill, London.

Taylor, R.P. (1988) An Artificial Intelligence Framework for Experimental Design and Analysis in Discrete Event Simulation. Unpublished PhD thesis. University of Warwick.

Taylor, R.P. and Hurrion, R.D. (1988) An expert advisor for simulation experimental design and analysis, in Artificial Intelligence and Simulation: The Diversity of Applications. Conference proceedings, (T. Henson, Ed.), The Society for Computer Simulation, San Diego.

3 Towards a statistic of metadata for knowledge analysis

E. Diday
University of Paris, Dauphine/INRIA

1 INTRODUCTION

In probability theory, very little is said about events which are generally identified to parts of the set of samples Ω. In computer science, object-oriented languages consider more general events called objects or "frames" defined by intention. In data analysis (multidimensional scaling, clustering, exploratory data analysis etc.) more importance is given to the elementary objects which belong to the sample Ω than in classical statistics where attention is focused on the probability laws of Ω; however, objects of data analysis are generally identified to the point of $\Re^p$ and hence are unable to treat complex objects or metadata coming for instance from large databases, and knowledge bases. Our aim is to define complex objects called "symbolic objects" inspired by those of object-oriented languages in such a way that "data analysis" (as, for instance, exploratory data analysis, factorial analysis, multi-dimensional scaling) becomes generalised in "knowledge analysis". Objects will be defined by intension by the properties of their extension. More precisely, we distinguish objects which "unify" rather than elementary observed objects which characterise "individual things" (their extension); for instance "the customers of my shop" instead of "a customer of my shop", "a specie of mushroom" instead of "the mushroom that I have in my hand".

The aim of this paper is to reduce the gap between statistics or data analysis (where people are not yet very interested in treating this kind of object) and artificial intelligence (where people are more interested in knowledge representation, reasoning and learning than in the extension of the data analysis to knowledge analysis).

2 BOOLEAN SYMBOLIC OBJECTS

We consider Ω a set of individual things called "elementary objects" and a set of descriptor functions $y_i: \Omega \to O_i$.

A basic kind of symbolic objects are "events". An event denoted $e_i = [y_i = V_i]$ where $V_i \subseteq O_i$ is a function $\Omega \to$ (true, false) such that $e_i(w) = $ true if $y_i(w) \in V_i$. When $y_i(w)$ has no sense (the kind of computer used by a company without computers $V_i = \phi$ and when it has a meaning but it is not known $V_i = O_i$. The extension of e_i in Ω denoted by $ext(e_i/\Omega)$ is the set of elements w $\in \Omega$ such that $e_i(w) = $ true.

An assertion is a conjunction of events $a = \underset{i}{\wedge} [y_i = V_i]$; the extension of a denoted $ext(a/\Omega)$ is the set of elements of Ω such that $\forall^i y_i(w) \in V_i$.

A "horde" is a symbolic object which appears for instance, when we need to express relations between parts of a picture that we wish to describe. More generally a horde is a function h from Ω^p in {true, false} such that $h = \underset{i}{\wedge} [y_i(u_i) = V_i]$ if $u = (u_i,...,u_p)$.

> For example; $h = [y_1(u_1) = 1] \wedge [y_2(u_2)=\{3,5\}] \wedge [y_3(u_1)=\{30,35\}] \wedge$ [neighbour $(u_1,u_2) = $ yes]; $h(v) = $ true where $v = (v_1, v_2)$ iff $y_1(v_1) = 1$, $y_2(v_2) \in \{3, 5\}$, $y_3(v_1) \in [30,35]$ and v_1, v_2 are neighnour

A synthesis object is a conjunction or a semantic link between hordes denoted in case of conjunction by $s = \hat{i} h_i$ where each horde may be defined on a different set Ω_i by different descriptors. For instance Ω_1 may be individuals, Ω_2 location, Ω_3 kind of job etc. All these objects are detailed in Diday (1991).

3   MODAL OBJECTS

Suppose that we wish to use a symbolic object to represent individuals satisfying the following sentence: "It is possible that their weight be between 300 and 500 grammes and their colour is often red or seldom white"; this sentence contains two evens $e_1 = [$wheight $= [300, 500]]$ and $e_2 = [$colour $= $ (red, white)] which lack the modes possible, often and seldom, a new kind of event, denoted f_1 and f_2, is needed if we wish to introduce them $f_1 = $ possible [height $= [300,500]]$ and $f_2 = [$colour $= \{$often red, seldom white$\}]$; we can see that f_1 contains an external mode possible affecting e_1 whereas f_2 contains internal modes affecting the values contained in e_2. Hence it is possible to describe informally the sentence by a modal assertion object denoted $a = f_1 \wedge_x f_2$ where $\wedge_x$ represents a kind of conjunction related to the background knowledge of the domain. The case of modal assertions of the kind $a = \underset{i}{\wedge} f_i$ where all the fi are events with external modes has been studied for instance in Diday (1990). This paper is devoted to the case where all the fi contain only internal modes, as f_2 in the preceding example.

4 INTERNAL MODAL OBJECTS

4.1 A Formal Definition of Internal Modal Objects

Let x be the background knowledge and
M^x a set of modes, for instance M^x = {often, sometimes, seldom, never}
or M^x = [0,1].

Q_i = {q_i^j}j a set of mappings q_i^j from O_i in M^x, for instance O_i = {red, yellow, green}.

M^x = {0.1} and q_i^j (red) = 0.1, q_i^j (yellow) = 0.3, q_i^j (green) = 1, where the meaning of the values of 0.1, 0.3, 1 depends on the background knowledge (for instance q_i^j may express a probability, see section 5.1, a possibility or a belief, see Diday (1993)).

y_i is a descriptor (the colour for instance); it is a mapping from Ω in Q_i. Notice that in the case of Boolean objects y_i was a mapping from Ω in O_i, and not Q_i.

Example: if O_i and M^x are chosen as in the previous example and the colour of w is red, then $y_i(\omega)$ = r means that $r \in Q_i$ be defined, for instance, by r(red) = 1, r(yellow) = 0, r(green) = 0.

OP_x = {$\cup_x$, $\cap_x$, c_x} where $\cup_x$, $\cap_x$ expresses a kind of union and intersection between subsets of Q_i and $c_x(q_i)$ (sometimes denoted $\bar{q}_i$, the complementary of $q_i \in Q_i$). The choice of OP_x must be coherent with the choice of Q_i.

Example: if $q_i^j \in Q_i$ and $Q_i^j \subseteq Q_i$

$$q_i^1 \cup_x q_i^2 = q_i^1 + q_i^2 - q_i^1 q_i^2$$
$$q_i^1 \cap_x q_i^2 = q_i^1 q_i^2 \text{ where } q_i^1 q_i^2(v) = q_i^1(v) q_i^2(v); \ c_x(q_i) = 1 - q_i$$
$$Q_i^1 *_x Q_i^2 = b(Q_i^1) *_x b(Q_i^2) \text{ where } *_x \in \{\cup_x, \cap_x\}$$

and
$$b(Q_i^j) = \{\cup_x q_i / q_i \in Q_i^j\} \text{ and } c_x(Q_i^j) = 1 - c_x(b(Q_i^j))$$

This choice of OP_x is "archimedian" because it satisfies a family of properties studied by Shweizer and Sklar (1960) and recalled by Dubois and

Prade (1988).

g_x is a "comparison" mapping from $Q_i \times Q_i$ in an ordered space L^x.

Example: $L^x = M^x = [0, 1]$ and $g_x (q_i^1, q_i^2) = <q_i^1, q_i^2> = \sum\{q_{i1(v)} q_{i2(v)}/v \in \theta_i\}$, the scalar product

f_x is an "aggregation" mapping from $P(L^x)$ the power set of L^x in L^x. For instance, $f_x (\{L_1,...,L_n\}) = \max L_i$.

Let $Y = \{y_i\}$ be a set of descriptors and $V = \{V_i\}$ a set of subsets of Q_i such that $V_i = (q_i^j) \subseteq Q$. Now we are able to give the formal definition of an internal object (called "im" object).

Definition of an im insertion

Given OP_x, g_x and f_x, and im object is a mapping a_{YV} from Ω W in L^x denoted $a = \underset{i}{\wedge} \{y_i = \{q_i^j\}_j\}$ such that if $\omega \in \Omega$ is described for any i by $y_i(\omega) = \{r_i^j\}$

then

$$a(\omega) = f_x(\{g_x (\underset{j}{\cup}_x q_i^j, \underset{j}{\cup}_x r_i^j)\}_i).$$

We denote by A_x the set of im objects associated to background knowledge x and ϕ the mapping from Ω in A_x such that $\phi(\omega) = \omega^s = \underset{i}{\wedge} x[y_i = y_i (\omega)]$.

4.2   Extension of im Objects

There are at least two ways to define the extension of an im object a. The first consists in considering that each element $\omega \in \Omega$ is more or less in the extension of a according to its weight given be $a(\omega)$; in that case the extension of a denoted Ext (a/ Ω) will be the set of couples $\{(\omega , a(\omega))/\omega \in \Omega\}$. The second requires a given threshold α and then the extension of a will be Ext$(a/\Omega ,\alpha) = \{\omega/\omega \in \Omega , a(\omega) \geq \alpha\}$.

4.3   Semantic of im Objects

In addition to the modes, several other notions may be expressed by an im object a:

1. Uncertainty: $a(\omega)$ is not true or false as for Boolean objects but it expresses a degree of uncertainty.

2. Variation: it appears at two levels, in an im object denoted $a = \underset{i}{\wedge}_x [y_i =$

$\{q_i^j\}_i]$; first in each q_i^j, for instance if y_i is the colour and q_i^1 (red) = 0.5, q_i^1 (green) = 0.3 it means that there exists a variation between the individual objects which belong into the extension of a (for instance a specie of mushrooms) where some are red and others are green; second, for given description y_i between the q_i^j (each q_i^j expresses for instance the variation in a different kind of specie).

3. Doubt: if we say that the colour of a specie of mushrooms is red "or" green, it is an "or" of variation, but if we say that the colour of the mushroom which is in my hand is red "or" green, it is an "or" of doubt.

Hence, if we describe $\omega \in \Omega$ by $\phi(\omega) = \omega^s = i\ [y_i = y_i(\omega)]$ where $y_i(\omega) = \{r_i^j\}_j$ we express a doubt in each r_i^j and among the r_i^j provided for instance by several experts. For more details, see Lebbe et al. (1990), Diday (1991).

4.4   An Example of Background Knowledge Expressing "Intensity"

Here the background knowledge x is denoted i for intensity. Each individual object $\omega \in \Omega$ is a manufactured object described by two features y_1 which express the degree of "roundness" and y_2 the "heaviness": $O_1 = \{$flat, round$\}$, $O_2 = \{$heavy$\}$; $M^i = \{$very, enough, a little, very little, nil$\}$.

Let a and ω^s be defined by:

$a = [y_1 = $ a little flat, enough round$] \wedge i\ [y_2 = $ a little heavy, enough heavy$]$.

$\omega^s = [y_1 = $ enough round$] \wedge i\ [y_2 = $ a little heavy, enough heavy$]$.

(The user has a doubt for ω between a little and enough heavy).

Hence q_1^1 (flat) = a little, q_1^1 (round) = enough, q_2^1 (heavy) = a little, r_1^1 (flat) = nil, r_1^1 (round) = enough, r_2^1 (heavy) = a little, r_2^2 (heavy) = enough.

A given taxonomy Tax which expresses the background knowledge on the values of M^i allows us to say that Tax (a little, enough) = almost; hence if we settle that $r_2^1 \cup_i r_2^2$ (v) = Tax (r_2^1 (v), r_2^2 (v)) we have $r_2^1 \cup_i r_2^2$ (heavy) = Tax (a little, enough) = almost.

We define L^i by L_1 = not acceptable, L_2 = acceptable, L_3 = completely acceptable and we suppose that the comparison mapping g_i is given by a table T_g such that $g_i(q_1^1 , r_1^1) = T_{gi}$ ((a little flat, enough round), (nil flat, enough round)) = acceptable and g_i (q_2^1 , $r_2^1 \cup_x r_2^2$) = T_{gi} (a little heavy, almost heavy) = not acceptable.

Finally if we settle f({L_i}) = min L_i and $L_1 < L_2 < L_3$ we obtain a(ω) = f_i (not acceptable, acceptable) = not acceptable.

5   PROBABILIST OBJECTS

5.1   The Probabilist Approach

First we recall the well-known axioms of Kolmogorov:

If C(Ω) is a σ-algebra on Ω (i.e. a set of subsets, stable for numerable intersection or union and for complementary), we say that p is a measure of probability on (Ω , C(Ω)) if

1. p(Ω) = 1
2. p($\cup_i A_i$) = Σ P(A_i) if $A_i \in$ C(Ω) and $A_i \cap A_j = \phi$.

There are several semantics which follow these axioms; for instance, luck in games, frequences, some kind of uncertainty. Let Q_i be a set of measure of probabilities defined on (O_i, C(O_i)); we make the assumption that $\forall \omega \in \Omega$, $\varphi(\omega) = \omega^s$ such that ω^s = i [y_i = $y_i(\omega)$] with $y_i(\omega) \in Q_i$.

Definition
A probabilist assertion is an im assertion which takes its values in Lpr = [0,1]

$$OP_{pr}: \forall q_i^1, q_i^2 \in Qi q_i^1 \cup_{pr} q_i^2 = q_i^1 + q_i^2 - q_i^1 q_i^2; \; q_i^1 \cap_{pr} q_i^2 = q_i^1 q_i^2$$

which is the mapping which associate at $v \in O_i$, $q_i^1(v) q_i^2(v)$;

$$g_{pr}: \forall q_i^1, q_i^2 \in Q_i \; g_{pr} (q_i^1, q_i^2) = <q_i^1 + q_i^2> = \Sigma \{q_i^1(v) q_i^2(v)/v \in \Omega\}.$$

$$f_{pr}: f_{pr}(\{L_i\}) = \text{mean of the } L_i$$

To give an inituitive idea of the notion of union of measure of probabilities it is easy to see that if q_i^1 and q_i^2 are the measure of probabilities associated to two dices, $q_i^1 \cup_{pr} q_i^2(V)$ is the probability that the event V occurs when the two dice are trialled independently in one die or (not exclusive) in the other. Notice that $q_i^1 \cup_{pr} q_i^2$ is not a measure of probability because even if $q_i^1 \cup_{pr} q_i^2(v) \in [0,1]$, the sum of the $q_i^1 \cup_{pr} q_i^2(v)$ on O_i is larger than 1 and also the sum of the $q_{i1} \cap_{pr} q_{i2(v)}$ on θ_i is smaller than 1. By the same way, it may be shown that $g_{pr}(q_{i1}, q_{i2})$ is the probability that both dices trialed independently give the same value.

5.2   Example

An object ω is described by its colour $y_1(\omega)$ which may be red or blue and its roundness $y_2(\omega)$ which may be round or flat.

Let $a = [y_1 = q_1^1, \ q_1^2] \wedge_{pr} [y_2 = q2]$ and $\omega^s = [y_1 = r_1] \wedge_{pr} [y_2 = r_2]$ where q_1^1 (red) $= 9.0$; q_1^1 (blue) $= 0.1$; q_1^2 (red) $= 0.5$; q_1^1 (blue) $= 0.5$; q_2 (round) $= 0.2$; q_2(flat) $= 0.8$. It results that a is described by two kinds of objects: either often red and rarely blue or red or blue with same probability.

By using $q_1^3 = q_1^1 \cup_{pr} q_1^2 = q_1^1 + q_1^2 - q_1^1 q_1^2$ we obtain q_1^3 (red) $= 0.9 + 0.5 - 0.9 \times 0.5 = 0.95$

$$q_1^3 \text{ (blue)} = 0.1 + 0.5 - 0.1 \times 0.5 = 0.55$$

We have also:

r_1 (red) $= 1$, r_1 (blue) $= 0$; r_2 (round) $= 1$, r_2 (flat) $= 0$

and then, it results that $a(\omega) = g_{pr}(q_1^3, r_1) \wedge_{pr} g_{pr}(q_2, r_2)$

$= (0.95 \times 1 + 0.55 \times 0) \wedge_{pr} (0.2 \times 1 + 0.8 \times 0)$

$= 0.95 \ \wedge_{pr} \ 0.20 = \frac{1}{2}(0.95 + 0.20) = 0.57$

which represents the average probability that an instance of the class of objects described by a be ω; it may be interpreted as a kind of membership degree of ω to the im object defined by a.

5.3   Kernel Objects, Credibility and Plausibility

Kernel objects are useful when probabilities are known only on some intervals. Given q_i a measure of probability on $(O_i, C(O_i)$, we denote $q_i^j(V) = q_i(V_j \cap V)$ and we suppose that the V_j are chosen such that $\sum_j q_i^j(V_j) = 1$. The q_i^j for a given set of $V_j \subseteq O_i$ are called kernels and we denote $Q_i = \{q_i^j\}_j$.

Definition

A kernel object denoted $a_k = \wedge_k[y_i = (q_i^j)_j]$ is an im assertion which takes its values in $L^k = [0,1]$ such that:

- OP_k: $\forall q_i^1, q_i^2 \in Q_i$ $\qquad q_i^1 \cup_k q_i^2 = q_i((V_1 \cup V_2) \cap V)$

  $q_i^1 \cap_k q_i^2(V) = q_i((V_1 \cap V_2) \cap V)$ and

  $c_k = (q_i^j)\, (V) = q_i(c(v_j) \cap V))$

- g_k : $g_k\,(q_i^1, q_i^2) = \dfrac{1}{q_i(V_1)}\, q_i\,(V_1 \cap V_2)$

- f_k is the mean

It results from this definition that if $a_k = [y_i = \{q_i^j\}_j]$ given $\omega \in \Omega$ such that $\omega^s = [y_i = r_i^l \ ]$ we have $a_k(\omega) = g_k(\{q_i^j\}_j, r_{il}\,) = \dfrac{1}{q_i(\cup V_j)}\, q_i(\underset{j}{\cup}\ V_j \cap U_l)$ if $r_i^l\ (V)$

$= r_i\ (U_l \cap V)$ where $r_i \in Q_i$.

In practice it may happen that we are able to know only the q_i^j and not q_i; in this case we may compute $a_k(\omega)$ by approximating q_i with a measure denoted $E_i^{\alpha,\ \beta}$ such that

$$E_i^{\alpha,\ \beta}(V) = \sum_j \{q_i^j(V_j)/d^o(V_j \cap V) \in I_{\alpha,\ \beta}\}$$

where $\alpha < \beta$ and $d_o(V_j \cap V)$ expresses a degree of intersection between V_j and V and $I_{\alpha,\ \beta} = [\alpha, \beta] \subseteq [0, 1]$ expresses that the intersection of V_j with V is between 100α and 100β per cent. If $\alpha = \beta = 1$, V_j is included in V and $E_i^{1,1}(V) = Bel(V)$ if the only constraint on α is $\alpha > 0$, $E_i^{\alpha,\beta}(V) = Pl(V)$ and Bel and Pl satisfy the axioms of belief and plausibility measures (see for instance Dempster (1990), Pearl (1990)), $\sum_j q_i^j(V_j) = 1$, $Bel_i(V) = \sum\{q_i^j(V_j)/V_j \subseteq V\}$, $Pl_i(V) = 1 -$ $Bel(c(V))$. It is also easy to see that $Bel < q_i < Pl$, if $\forall j, 1\ V_j \cap V_l = \varnothing$.

5.4   Example

An expert describes a species of mushrooms by saying that it is seldom red and often pink or grey; this is represented by the kernel object a = [y₁ = q^1_1, q^2_1] with V_1 = {red}, V_2 = {pink, grey} and $q^1_1(V_1)$ = 0.1, $q^2_1(V_2)$ = 0.8; a given mushroom which is red, pink or brown (there is doubt) is represented by ω^s = [y₁ = r^3_1] with $r^3_1(V_3)$ = 0.8 and V_3 = {red, pink, brown}. Then

$$a(\omega) = g(q^1_1 \cup q^2_1, r^3_1) = \frac{1}{q_i(V_1 \cup V_2)} q_i(V_1 \cup V_2 \cap V_3) = \frac{1}{q_i(V_1 \cup V_2)} q_i(V)$$

with V = {red, pink}. If q_i is approximated by $E^{\alpha,\beta}$ we have $q_i(V)$ = $E^{\alpha,\beta}(V)$; the intersection between V_1 and V is 100 per cent as $V_1 \cap V$ = {red} and between V_2 and V is 50 per cent as $V_2 \cap V$ = {pink}; therefore, with $\alpha \le 0.5$,

$$a(\omega) = \frac{1}{q_i(V_1 \cup V_2)} (q^1_1(V_1) + q^2_1(V_2)) = \frac{0.9}{0.9} = 1$$

is the plausibility for ω to be in the species described by a; with $\alpha > 0.5$

$$a(\omega) = \frac{1}{q_i(V_1 \cup V_2)} q^1_1(V_1) = \frac{0.1}{0.9} = 0.11$$

is the credibility of ω to be in the same species.

6   THE PARTICULAR CASE OF BOOLEAN OBJECTS

A boolean object a = $\wedge_i$ [y₁ = V_i] is an im object a_b = $\wedge_i$ [y₁ = q_i] where q_i is the characteristic mapping of V_i in O_i, OP_b = {$\cup_b$, $\cap_b$, c_b} is such that $q_1 \cup_b q_2$ = max(q_1, q_2), $q_1 \cap_b q_2$ = min(q_1, q_2) and $c_b(q)$ = 1− q; $g_b(q_i, r_i)$ = <q_i, r_i> and f_b = min; it results that if it exists only a single $v \in O_i$ such that $r_i(v) \ne 0$ then $a_b(\omega)$ = 1 (thus $r_i \le q_i$) $\Leftrightarrow$ a(ω) = true and then $a_b(\omega)$ = 0 $\Leftrightarrow$ a(ω) = false.

7   SOME QUALITIES AND PROPERTIES OF SYMBOLIC OBJECTS

7.1   Order, Union and Intersection between in Objects

It is possible to define a partial preorder $\le_\alpha$ on the im objects by stating that: $a_1 \le_\alpha a_2$ iff $\forall \omega \in \Omega \alpha \le a_1(\omega) \le a_2(\omega)$.

We deduce from this preorder an equivalence relation R by a_1 R a_2 iff Ext(a_1/Ω, α) = Ext(a_2/Ω, α) and a partial order denoted $\le_\alpha$ and called "symbolic order" on the equivalence classes induced from R.

We say that a_1 inherits from a_2 or that a_2 is more general than a_1, at the level α, iff $a_1 \le_\alpha a_2$.

The symbolic union $a_1 \cup_x a_2$ (resp. intersection $a_1 \cup_x a_2$) at the level α is the conjunction $\wedge_x$ of the im objects b such that Ext $(a_1/\Omega, a) \cup$ Ext$(a_2/\Omega, \alpha)$ $\subseteq$ Ext$(b/\Omega, \alpha)$ (resp. Ext$(a1/\Omega, \alpha) \cap$ Ext$(a2/\Omega, \alpha) \subseteq$ Ext$(b/\Omega, \alpha)$.

7.2   Some Qualities of Symbolic Objects

As in the Boolean case, see Brito and Diday (1990), it is possible to define different kinds of qualities of symbolic objects (refinement, simplicity, completeness ...).

For instance, we say that a symbolic object s is complete if the properties which characterize its extension are exactly those whose conjunction defines the object. However, intuitively if I see white dogs in my street and I state "I see dogs", my statement doesn't describe the dogs in a complete way, since I am not saying that they are white.

On the other hand, the simplicity at level α of an im object is the smallest number of elemen tary events whose extension at level α coincides with the extension of s at the same level.

7.3   Some Properties of im Objects

It may be shown (see Diday (1993)) that given a level α the set of im objects is a lattice for the symbolic order and that the symbolic union and intersection define the supermum and infimum of any couple. It may also be shown that the symbolic union and intersection of complete im objects are complete im objects and hence that the set of complete im objects is also a lattice.

8   AN EXTENSION OF PROBABILITY THEORY

The notions of σ-algebra, measure and the Kolmogorov axioms may be extended (see Diday 1991) in at least two ways.

1.   The set of samples Ω will be the set of im objects a_x.

2.   The usual operators OP $= \{\cup, \cap, C\}$ of classical set theory will be replaced by $OP_x = \{\cup_x, \cap_x, C_x\}$ adapted to the background knowledge.

More Precisely we get the following extensions associated with a background knowledge (b.k.)$_x$.

Definition

A σ-algebra $C_x(E)$ on a set E provided with $OP_x = \{\cup_x, \cap_y, C_x\}$ is a set of subsets of E such that:

(i) $E \in C_X(E)$

(ii) $\forall E_i \in C_X(E)$, $C_X(E_i) \in C_X(E)$

(iii) any enumerable sequence $\{E_i\}$ of subsets of E is such that
$\cap_X E_i \in C_X(E)$.
    i

Definition

A probability measure q_X on $(E, C_X(E))$ is a mapping q_X from $C_X(E)$ in $[0, 1]$ such that:

(i) $q_X(E) = 1$

(ii) $\forall E_1, E_2 \in C_X(E)$, $q_X(E_1 \cup_X E_2) = q_X(E_1) + q_X(E_2) - q_X(E_1 \cap_X E_2)$

Definition

A random variable X from $(E, C_X(E), q_X)$ in $(F, C_X(F))$ is a mapping from $(E, C_X(E))$ in $(F, C_X(F))$ such that $\forall F_i \in C_X(F)$, $X^{-1}(F_i) \in C_X(E)$.

Such a random variable induces a mapping called the "law of X" denoted q_X^X, which is a mapping from $C_X(F)$ in $[0, 1]$ such that $q_X^X(F_i) = q_X(X^{-1}(F_i))$.

It may then be shown that if $X^{-1}(F_i *_X F_j) = X^{-1}(F_i) *_X X^{-1}(F_j)$ for $*_X \in \{\cup_X, \cap_X\}$ then the law of X is a probability measure on $(E, C_X(E))$.

We use those definitions to extend an im assertion $a = \wedge [y_i = q_i]$ to a dual
                                          i
im assertion denoted a* defined on subsets of $\mathbf{a}_X$ the set of im assertion. More precisely:

Notice that it may be shown in the case of kernel objects that OP_X is an idempotent algebra whereas in case of probabilist objects, OP_X is archimedian.

Given $A \subseteq \mathbf{a}_X$ we denote $a*_l$ a "dual" measure of $a_l = \wedge_X [y_i = q_i^l]$ and
                                                                   i
Q_i^A the set of q_i^l such that $a = \wedge_X [y_i = q_i^l] \in A$, and we settle
                                                i

$$a*_l(A) = f_X((g_X(q_i^l, \{\cup_X q_i^l/q_i^l \in Q_i^A\}_i))$$
                                              j

Then, it may be shown that a* is the law of a random variable X from $(Q_X,$

$C_x(Q_x, q_x^*)$ in (a_x, C_x, a_x) where q_x^* is a probability measure defined on Q_x, the set of $q^1 = \{q_i^1\}i$ mappings. hence, in the case of probabilist or kernel objects we get the following result.

Theorem

1. $a^* (a_x) = 1$ and
2. $\forall A_1, A_2 \in a_x \ a^*(A_1 \cup_x A_2) = a^*(A_1) + a^*(A_2) - a^*(A_1 \cap_x A_2)$.

The proof of this theorem is easy in the case of kernel objects; in case of probabilist objects it may be found in Diday (1993).

Finally it appears that a^* is a kind of probability in case of probabilist objects. In the same way, we have defined possibilist and credibilist im objects a_{pos} and a_{cred}; it can then be shown that a^*_{pos} is a kind of possibility and that a^*_{cred} is a kind of credibility, for instance, when any $a_{cred} \in a$ has same focal element (see Diday (1993)).

9   STATISTICS AND DATA ANALYSIS OF SYMBOLIC OBJECTS

Several works have been recently carried out in this field; for histograms of symbolic objects, see De Carvalho et al. (1990) and (1991); for generating rules by decision graph on im objects in the case of possibilist objects with typicalities as modes see Lebbe and Vignes (1990); for generating overlapping clusters by pyramids see Brito and Diday (1990).

More generally, four kinds of data analysis may roughly be defined depending on the input and output; (a) numerical analysis of classical data arrays, (b) numerical analysis of symbolic objects (for instance by defining distances between objects), (c) symbolic analysis of classical data arrays (for instance obtaining a factor analysis or a clustering automatically interpreted by symbolic objects), (d) symbolic analysis of symbolic objects where the input of the methods are symbolic objects.

10   CONCLUSION

Unlike most of the work carried out in expert systems, symbolic data analysis constitutes a "critique of pure reasoning" by giving less importance to the inference engine and more importance to the study of the knowledge base, considered as a set of "symbolic objects". A wide field of research is opened by extending classical statistics to statistics of metadata and more more specially by extending problems, methods and algorithms of data analysis to symbolic objects.

REFERENCES

Brito, P. and Diday, E. (1990) Pyramidal representation of symbolic objects, in NATO ASI Series, Vol. F61 Knowledge Data and Computer-assisted Decisions, edited by Schader and Gaul. Springer Verlag.

Dempster, A.P. (1990) Construction and local computation aspects of network belief functions, in Influence Diagram, Belief Nets, and Decision Analysis, Wiley, New York, chapter 6.

Diday, E. (1990) Knowledge representation and symbolic data analysis, in NATO ASI Series, Vol. F61 Knowledge Data and Computer-assisted Decisions edited by Schader and Gaul. Springer Verlag.

Diday, E. (1991) Objects modaux pour l'analyse des connaissances, Rapport INRIA, Rocquencourt, 78150, France.

Diday, E. (1993) Probabilist, possibilist and belief objects for knowledge analysis, to appear in Annals of Operational research.

Dubois, D. and Prade, H. (1988) Possibility theory, Plenum New York.

Lebbe, J., Vignes, R. and Darmoni, S. (1990) Symbolic numeric approach for biological knowledge representation: a medical example with creation of identification graphs, in Proc. of Conf. on Data Analysis, Learning Symbolic and Numerical Knowledge, Antibes, ed. E. Diday, Nova Science Publishers, Inc., New York.

Pearl, J. (1990) Reasoning with belief functions: an analysis of compatibility, Int. Journal of Approximate reasoning, vol. 4, No. 5/6, p. 363.

Schafer, G. (1976) A Mathematical Theory of evidence, Princeton University Press.

Zadeh, L. (1971) Quantitative fuzzy semantics, Information Sciences, 159–176.

4 Simulation of uncertainty: decision support in complex incompletely defined environments

M. von Rimscha
CAD CAM CONCEPTS

1 DESIGNING THE MODEL – USER REQUIREMENTS

One of the central issues in forecasting and risk assessment is the proper choice of an abstract model which captures the uncertainty within the application problem in an appropriate way.

Traditionally the modelling of uncertainty was an extrapolation of observations in the past into the future. For this one could successfully employ statistical methods. In this context uncertainty is rather well understood – though one does not know the actual outcome of a single experiment or measurement, one knows the probability of its outcome, i.e. repeating that experiment several times would lead to a stable distribution of outcomes.

This statistical approach is very well suited for modelling the uncertainty of events which occur rather often under similar conditions – typical examples would be quality control or the insurance of standard risks.

There are, however, other notions of uncertainty which cannot be properly represented by a statistical model such as vagueness or lack of information.

Vagueness occurs quite usually in our everyday speech in formulations like: "The man is fairly tall"; "It is not likely to rain before dark"; "It is possibly cancer". Note that in these examples one has a combination of vague notions like "tall", "dark", "cancer" and vague qualifiers like "fairly", "before" and "possibly". These kind of formulations are not just "lazy" statements which could be refined if necessary, but reflect in many cases the actual knowledge of the speaker.

Vagueness can be seen as a special case of lack of information, which, obviously, can also occur in situations described by precise notions.

If one wants to capture the knowledge of experts within a computerised system, it is essential that the vagueness or the lack of information is adequately represented. One of the shortcomings of present knowledge acquisition is the demand of most systems for exact statements or for complete probability distributions. Thus the expert is forced to decide on precise values, which are then further processed by the systems leading to exact answers. The user of such systems gets, in this way, an unjustified impression of certainty.

In order to handle uncertainty in the sense of vagueness or lack of knowledge properly, users would require a knowledge-based system with the following characteristics:

- The user is able to introduce vague notions and can declare their logical relationship to each other without being forced to model these numerically.
- The user can combine exact logical knowledge with soft judgemental knowledge.
- The user can introduce statistical numerically described knowledge.
- The user can interrogate the knowledge base in his own vague terms, in logical terms, or in a numerically oriented way.
- The system integrates the various sorts of rules, facts and conjectures in a coherent, unified way such that each answer to an enquiry takes into account all information of whatever character.
- The system does not add structural knowledge, i.e. no assumptions are made that add implicitly to the given body of knowledge.

A good application-oriented survey about the handling of uncertainty in expert systems and about appropriate user interfaces can be found in (Wensley89).

2   THE APPROACHES TOWARDS MODELLING UNCERTAINTY

In this section we shall examine the main approaches towards the representation of uncertainty. It will become clear that each of these approaches has its merits but also its shortcomings. A synthesis of these different methods will be described in the next section.

2.1   Classical Statistics

As mentioned above, the traditional approach to uncertainty is the use of statistical methods. Here one deals with a well understood, mature methodology, where an abundance of commercial software is available. It should be observed, however, that the sort of uncertainty which should be modelled via statistical models is of a special nature.

Roughly speaking, statistics deal with repeated events or with collectives of objects that share to some extent common characteristics. In this sense statistics are retrospective, as they build on given data and extrapolate from them future trends or the properties of analogous collectives. This method has been proven successful for a wide range of applications in natural science, social sciences and finance. Nevertheless there are some problems, not with the statistical method itself but with its use:

1. The justification of the underlying model may be of a rather subjective nature, i.e. the definition of a model of a very complex scenario or of a scenario which might be subject to abrupt changes depending on human decisions or on not fully understood combinations of reasons is a rather speculative endeavour.

2. The mapping of balanced ignorance onto balanced probabilities known as the indifference principle, adds "knowledge" to the model which is justified only by the desire to present "decent results". It is well known that, the system analysts, because their statistical methods need that, force their clients to come up with exact numbers, which in the best case could be interpreted as the "mean value" of the interval of ignorance.

Both problems originate from the desire for predictions represented by exact numbers. The honest answer "we only know very little about the problem" is usually not acceptable to the high-flying decision maker. This is not to blame the principally sound methods of statistics but only the uncritical use of it. In fact the difficulties of applying the frequency-oriented statistical approach to situations, where singular events or individual decisions come into the game, have been recognised by the statistical community for a long time – it leads to the approach of subjective probabilities to be described in the next section.

2.2 Subjective Probability

Subjective probability deals with the formal description and combination of more or less vague judgements, i.e. it attempts to describe degrees of belief, likelihoods, etc., in the numerically oriented language of probability theory. That the notion of probability has an objective, frequency-oriented meaning but just as well a subjective, belief-oriented meaning, has been discussed by various authors since the very beginning of the emergence of probability theory. The other source for subjective probability was the development of formal logic, where also early attempts were made to handle uncertain judgements. A comprehensive overview about the various approaches to subjective probability one finds in (Kyburg/Smokler80).

It should be emphasised that the degrees of belief or likelihoods are not to be mixed up with truth-values. A judgement will in the end be true or false, though one might not be in the position to ever decide that. The degree of belief is not measuring the truth but instead the weight of evidence that a statement or judgement is true. In this sense subjective probability – just as statistics – leaves the laws of classical logic untouched but introduces the uncertainty on a meta-level. In this sense subjective probability degree of belief has to be clearly distinguished from any "fuzzy" approach dealing with intermediate truth-values (see below).

There have been various formalisations of subjective probability, some of them reformulating classical, frequency-oriented probability theory for the subjective setting, others working with lower and upper probabilities and finally some which look at probabilities in a qualitative, i.e. non-numeric, way, which means that one deals with (partial) order of probability values only (for an extensive treatment of this topic see (Fine73).

For similar reasons as in statistics also in subjective probability theory there is the tendency to introduce extra conditions and rules which might in special applications be sensible but which in general constitute an unjustified extension of the given knowledge. A typical example in this context would be the combination rule in the Demoster/Shafer approach to lower and upper probability (see Shafer75) and for a critical review (Weichselberger/ Pöhlmann90); a prototype implementation of that approach is described in (Lowrance86). Rules of this sort can be seen as the counterpart to the ad hoc combination of derivation rules within fuzzy logic. We shall look into this in more detail in the next section.

2.3   The Logical Approach

Another way to get to grips with the unknown was to analyse and formalise the usual language. This leads over time to a broad range of formalisms, whose proponents had and have still good times to fight for. The problem here seems to be that the stronger and more refined the logical machinery for the modelling of uncertainty becomes, the less connection there is to the vague argumentation lines in everyday situations. Below we shall look at some of these formalisations:

1. Classical propositional or first-order predicate logic, here one deals with formulas, which are either true or false or whose truth-value cannot be decided on the basis of the given knowledge. These sorts of logics are rather close to usual everyday reasoning and thus easy to understand, however, the handling of uncertainty is restricted to the "is undecidable" mode.

2. Modal logic, where one deals with quantifiers like "it is possible that" or "it is necessary that". Quantifiers of this sort obviously open up the road for a much more sophisticated dealing with uncertainty. Unfortunately the meaning of these quantifiers is also rather hazy; therefore, quite a lot of

modal logics have been developed, which use these quantifiers with quite different semantics. Thus for the non-initiated user of such a logic there is the danger that his intentions and derivations are not reflected by the logic he uses. Another problem with these logics is that the degrees of uncertainty are very coarse, i.e. if one knows rather exactly the degree of likelihood of some statements there is no natural way to map this more specific knowledge into the modal logic framework. An example for an expert system using modal quantifiers is given in (Ellam/Maisey87).

3. Fuzzy logic is an interesting approach to combine the logical derivation methods with numerical representations as in probability theory. In fact there are two layers to fuzzy representations:

The verbose fuzziness occurring in phrases like "it is not excluded that"; "one might assume that"; or "it is fairly safe to assume that"; "is rather small".

The exact fuzziness represented by functions that map certain events or sets into the interval (0.1) thus describing the degree of certainty that some element belongs to that event/set or not.

These modes are connected by rules that transfer verbose descriptions into functions.

Obviously, there are some problems with this approach. First of all there is no consensus about the semantic of the verbose fuzzy phrases. Think of a formulation like "what you have done there is not too bad" – this might be a glorious laudatio or, uttered by somebody else, an extremely skeptical evaluation. It has in fact been found out that the attachment of probability values or likelihoods to certain phrases varies considerably so that verbose fuzzy statements become difficult to interpret without their context.

Therefore the proponents of fuzzy logic quite rightly emphasises that a fuzzy system has to be attuned to the specific application. But as the vague clauses are fairly (another one) personality dependent in their meaning, a system would have to be attuned to the specific users of that system, which would restrict the practical usefulness considerably.

In the end this means that for a general-purpose fuzzy system, one should get rid of the verbose formulations, but use numerical representations instead (this does not preclude dedicated applications which might present the user with some words instead of numbers, if it is ensured that either the user or the system analyst, who watched the user and set up those words and their mapping onto numbers, use these words in accordance with their underlying numerical meaning.

The use of "exact" fuzzy descriptions or statements is also not without problems. First of all: How to get there? i.e. how to determine your function into [0.1] on the basis of which data. If you do it on the basis of statistical data, why not use the powerful, though mathematically more demanding tools of classical statistics? But assuming there are solid reasons for using fuzzy functions, the next step is to combine the knowledge according to "combination rules". There are a lot of them around and again one might find for each specific rule an application where this rule might fit. This fitting of rules has, however, nothing to do with logic anymore but expresses specialised application knowledge.

For a more enthusiastic description or the fuzzy-approach see (Graham/ Jones88).

Looking at the various logical approaches to grasping the concept of uncertainty, one might conclude that the classical logics are well understood in their naive meaning but insufficient to model uncertainty in a satisfying way, whereas the more elaborate methods of modal or fuzzy logics are still in the experimental stage or dedicated towards very specific applications. A good survey about the relations between expert systems and statistical modelling techniques is given in (Clark90).

3   SIMULATION OF UNCERTAINTY - SYNTHESIS AND IMPLEMENTATION

In this section there is described a methodology for dealing with uncertainty which combines the soundness of classical logic and statistics with the ability to handle approximative or qualitative knowledge. The underlying theoretical background has been independently developed in various places, see (Nilsson86), (Paaß88), (Rimscha83), (Andersen/Hooker90), and is in the meantime known as Probabilistic Logic.

The first (academic) implementation of this approach has been done in 1985 at Stuttgart University and ran on a mainframe (see Köbler85). As the computational power of small machines has since then increased sufficiently, it is now possible to provide this method commercially even on a PC (for a review of the system SIMUNC – stands for "SIMulation of UNCertainty" – see (Bartram90).

The first step, before using a computer at all, is to analyse the given problem and to structure your knowledge accordingly, i.e. identifying input parameters, output parameters, contingency conditions, transition functions etc. – in the next section we shall illustrate this with the help of a case study.

Your body of knowledge can be separated in two clearly identifiable parts:
*   The certain knowledge, this is the knowledge about which you are sure and which is stated as facts or rules (e.g. "The budgeted investment of company A exceeds £1M" or "If the new environmental legislation gets through, then factory B has to close down its present production").

- The probabilistic knowledge: this knowledge sits on top of the certain knowledge. It attaches probabilities to events which occur in the certain knowledge (e.g. "the probability that the new environmental legislation gets through is between 30% and 50%"), compares the likelihood of events (e.g. "It is more likely that factory B closes down than that factory A closes down" or conditions probabilities or values on the occurrence of events (e.g. "If the interest rate exceeds 16% the probability of the new environmental law getting through falls below 10%" or "In the case that factory A closes the emission of SO2 would be reduced between 20% and 25%").

Note that both sorts of knowledge are completely integrated with each other, i.e. when inquiring the knowledge base the logical closure of both the certain and the probabilistic knowledge is interrogated. Figure 1 gives an indication of the internal architecture of SIMUNC.

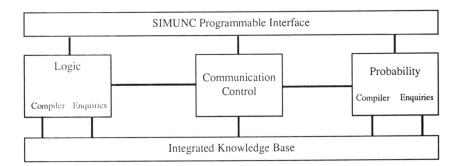

Figure 1

Though for the user the whole approach seems to be rule based, this method works according to quite different paradigms.

Run-Time Aspects:
In RULE-BASED Systems the complexity grows "rapidly" with the number of rules (because of backtracking and forward chaining).

In SIMUNC the complexity grows linearly with the number of probability statements, but can be reduced by increasing the number of logical dependencies between events.

Knowledge Representation:

In RULE-BASED Systems the rules are stored as declared by the user or as inbuilt by the system designer or knowledge engineer.

In SIMUNC the given knowledge – including the rules – is transformed into a comprehensive geometrical structure, which represents the logical closure of the knowledge and allows comparatively fast enquiries at any time. In this sense the given knowledge is stored in an at least partially pre-compiled form.

Algorithmic Aspects:

RULE-BASED Systems work with discrete methods, and have no problem with numerical instabilities or ambiguities. The disadvantage of this approach is that the integration of numerically given conditions and constraints is rather cumbersome and often fairly ad hoc (for a critical survey, see (Weichsel berger/Pöhlmann90)).

SIMUNC also uses discrete methods in its "logical" part. The difference in the SIMUNC approach is that these methods are then used to set up a framework for a geometrical construction within which the probability conditions are represented. Thus the numerical methods of the probability part are conceptually embedded into an underlying logic. The mathematics used follow the methods commonly used in operations research (for background information the reader should consult (Rimscha90)).

The method presented is surely not a universal tool to solve all the world's problems, but there are certain characteristics which might indicate that an application should be tackled with SIMUNC:

- The logical relation between the events is only partially known, i.e. one may know that x can only happen if y or z happen but have no idea to what extent y and z overlap.
- There is a mixture of precise numerical information that might be obtained by statistical methods or derived from the laws of nature, and of vague judgements which can be mapped (by the user) onto exact numbers only in a rather artificial way.
- Numerical information does not give rise to exact values or complete probability distributions, but consists at least partially only of lower and upper boundaries for values or probabilities.
- Judgements about likelihoods or preferences cannot be completely ordered in a unique way.

To make SIMUNC methodology available to non-numerate end users, the mathematical machinery (provided as a C-library) has to be concealed with an application layer which is tailored to the specific needs of the given problem. Figure 2 shows SIMUNC as part of an overall system integrating various problem-solving components.

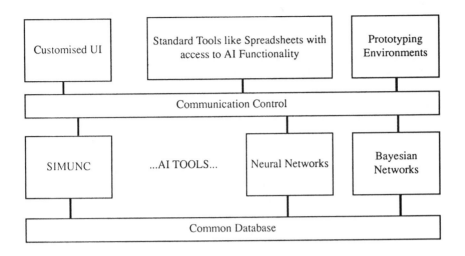

Figure 2

4   CASE STUDIES

4.1   SIMUNC in Banking Applications: Simulation of Creditworthiness

Scenario: A bank has to make up its mind about the credit limit of one of their major clients, say a machine tool factory.

The "naive" analysis:
Known to the bank are the current credit limit, the own capital/securities of the client, the present profit of the business and the actual market share whereby the market share is to be taken with a grain of salt as different analysts work with different segmentations of the market and come to varying conclusions.

Furthermore, the bank can identify certain factors, that might influence the development of that machine tool factory over the next few years. Examples might be: The development of the interest rate, the development of the machine tool market as a whole environment's legislation leading to a redirection of investment and higher production costs, industrial action, etc. These sort of factors vary over time and can only be roughly estimated.

Eventually the bank will have an idea how flexibly the factory can react to new developments, to which extent profit is likely to be reinvested and whether the client will be able to raise own further capital. Again information like this is rather soft and can only be given roughly, or one has to play through various alternatives.

All these factors are more or less dependent on each other and on the basis of these one wants to get an idea about the future financial development of that factory, in order to determine a sensible credit frame for it.

Mapping your analysis onto SIMUNC:
The knowledge described above is mapped onto SIMUNC by translating plain English statements or mathematical formulas describing dependencies between quantities into SIMUNC statements; these might be definite rules that relate events to each other (like: if interest rate is high then machine tool market shrinks), or it might be statements regarding the likelihood of some event in case something else happens (like: provided that the client takes over the ABC-group, his market share will rise to at least 40%; or, the likelihood that the client makes no profit within the next year is more than 80%, in that case the present management has to resign under the pressure of industrial action).

The bank manager using SIMUNC should, however, not be bothered with the intricacies of some technical language. As the underlying pattern of contingency is applicable to quite a broad class of cases, it is possible to provide a standard input methodology that allows an end-user input which is comparable to a usual spreadsheet input.

In fact the user will deal with a database of relevant parameters and with building blocks of information, that relates these parameters to each other. He will choose these building blocks according to information like: Is the client the market leader? Is the technology within that market likely to undergo major changes within the next 24 months? The system will in turn prompt the user to give some extra facts or assumptions to complete these building blocks (like: Rate the quality of the sales organisation of the client by a value between 0 and 9; or, is the present management likely to change to new technology in due time (rating between 0 and 9 again)?).

On the basis of this input the translation into SIMUNC statements can be done automatically.

Simulating with SIMUNC:
After having mapped your problem onto SIMUNC, you want to play through the possible scenarios of your problem, vary input parameters, look at the problem under special hypotheses, or simulate a development over time.

For this you may combine your building blocks by connecting their output parameters with the input parameters of other building blocks or even with its own input parameters (time delay required – see Figure 3). In this way you are able to follow up the propagation of your initial input data through a probabilistic network, whereby this propagation might be logical only (i.e. all statements and probabilities refer to the same point in time) or might be distributed over time. In this second case one has to take special care in case of complex feedback loops in order to make sure that the time-wise synchronisation of parameters is guaranteed.

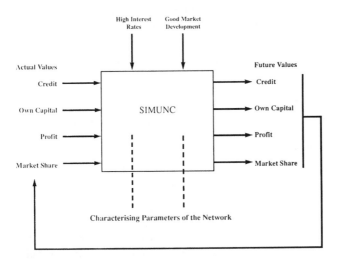

Feedback into Simulation of following Year

4.2 Using SIMUNC for Planning a Fault Diagnosis Network

Figure 4 represents a network consisting of a number of processing units which might be subject to failures in operation (e1-e3) and processing operations may trigger an alarm, and false alarms may also occur. The objective of the planner is to design a system that will give as good an indication as possible of where a fault may be.

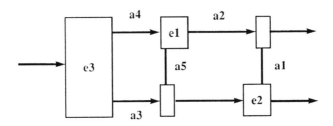

Figure 4

Thus the problem is to assess the likelihood of failures in case of more alarms coming on, and the likelihood of alarms getting on in case of certain combinations or failures.

Identifying the exact knowledge about the network:
Some information is known definitely to the planner. This is the certain or 'event' knowledge. For example, alarms are not independent but are connected as follows:

1. If a5 is on, then at least one of a2 and a3 will also come on.
2. a3 and a4 will never come on simultaneously.
3. If a1 come on, a2 will also come on.
4. If neither a2 nor a4 are on, then a5 will not come on.

Failures are also connected to one another:

5. If e3 occurs, then at least one of e1 and e2 happens too.
6. e2 and e3 cannot occur simultaneously.
7. e1 and e2 cannot occur simultaneously.

Finally, rules can be stated that connect the failures with the alarm devices. Usually these will be of a probabilistic nature, but some are definitely valid, e.g:

8. If failure e3 occurs, then a3 will never come on.
9. If none of e1, e2 and e3 occurs, then a3 and a2 will not come on simultaneously.

Modelling the exact knowledge in SIMUNC:
Statements given in the above rules can be compactly expressed in SIMUNC (without going into details here, one might note for the understanding of the formulas the following interpretation rules:
"*" = and / "#" = or / "<" = is included in / "-" = not / "0" = the impossible event / "=" = is equal to):

1.	a5	<	a2#a3
2.	a3*a4	=	0
3.	a1	<	a2
4.	-a4*-a2	<	-a5
5.	e3	<	e1#e2
6.	e2*e3	=	0
7.	e1*e2	=	0
8.	e3	<	-a3
9.	-e3*-e1*-e2*	<	-(a3*a1)

Enquiring the exact knowledge about the network:
From just the exact or "event" knowledge, certain questions can already be answered, e.g.:

Can e3 have failed if alarm a5 is on but a2 not?   (No)

Would a simultaneous failure of e3 and e2 trigger alarm a3?   (No)

If a1, a2 and a5 are all on does this imply that:

Some failures occurred?	(Yes)
e1 or e2 occurred?	(Yes)
e1 occurred?	(No)
e2 or e3 occurred?	(No)

Identifying the probabilistic knowledge about the network:
In addition to the certain knowledge, the planner will also have probabilistic data at his disposal, firstly regarding the likelihood of a failure when certain alarms are triggered, e.g.

1. If a4 comes on, the probability of e1 having failed is > 10%.

2. If a4 is not on, the probability of e1 having failed is < 1%.

3. The probability of e2 having failed is 12% if alarm a1 is on.

Also the relations between the alarms may be relevant, e.g.

4. a2 is more than twice as likely to come on as a1.

Similarly statements can be formulated concerning the likelihood of an alarm coming on if a failure has occurred, e.g.

5. The probability of e1 coming on is 70% if both e1 and e2 occur.

Modelling the probabilistic knowledge in SIMUNC:
SIMUNC statements expressing the above statements would be:

1. e1 > 0.1 /   a4
2. e1 < 0.01 / -a4
3. e2 = 0.12 / a1
4. a2 > 2a1
5. a1 > 0.7 /   e1*e2

Enquiring the integrated knowledge base of SIMUNC:
From a model of the above kind, the planner can now ask a whole range of questions such as:

- Which combinations of failures lead with what probability to certain combinations of alarms.
- With what probability are failures indicated by certain combinations or alarms.
- What is the likelihood of false alarms.

Note that these enquiries take into account both the exact and the probabilistic knowledge.

As the answers to these questions emerge, the planner is likely to want to vary his model to check the effects of various 'what if' attempts to improve its responsiveness. SIMUNC will perform consistency checks at every stage of the operation to ensure that new data does not contradict the existing model, and if an inconsistency does occur, will enable the user to locate that inconsistency precisely.

REFERENCES

Andersen, K. A. and Hooker, J. N. (1990) Bayesian Logic; Working paper 1-90-91, Graduate School of Industrial Administration, Carnegie Mellon University, Pittsburgh. PA 15213, USA.

Bartram, P. (1990) Risk Analysis; Executive Systems International 2, (8), pp. 5–7.

Clark, D. A. (1990) Human Expertise, Statistical Models and Knowledge-Based Systems; in Expertise and Decision Support, eds. G. Wright and F. Bolger; Plenum Press.

Ellam, S. and Maisey, M. N. (1987) A Knowledge-Based System to Assist in Medical Image Interpretation: Design and Evaluation Methodology; in Research and Development in Expert Systems III, ed. M. A. Bramer; Cambridge University Press.

Fine, T. L. (1973) Theories of Probability; Academic Press, New York.

Graham, I. and Jones, P. L. (1988) Expert Systems – Knowledge, Uncertainty and Decision; Chapman and Hall, London.

Köbler, J. (1985) Ein Programm zur Deduktion qualitativer und numerischer Wahrscheinlichkeiten; Studienarbeit, Institut für Informatik der Universität Stuttgart.

Kyburg, Jr., H. and Smokler, H. eds. (1980) Studies in Subjective Probability, 2nd ed.; Huntingdon, New York.

Lowrance, J. D. (1986) Automating Argument Construction; Journal of Statistical Planning and Inference, 20, 369–387.

Nilsson, N. J. (1986) Probabilistic Logic; Artificial Intelligence 28, pp. 71–87.

Paaß, G. (1988) Probabilistic Logic; in Non-Standard Logics for Automated Reasoning, eds. P. Smets, A. Mamdani, D. Dubois, H. Prade; Academic Press, London, pp. 213–252.

Rimscha, M. V. (1983) A Logical Approach to Non-Numerical Probability; Abstract of an invited paper of the 7th International Congress of Logic, Methodology and Philosophy of Science, Salzburg; Conference Abstracts, Vol. 1, pp. 252–254.

Rimscha, M. V. (1990) The Determination of Comparative and Lower Probability; Proceedings of the workshop on Uncertainty in Knowledge-Based Systems at the FAW in Ulm; FAW-B-90025, Vol. 2, pp. 344–376.

Shafer, G. (1975) A Mathematical Theory of Evidence; Princeton University Press.

Weichselberger, K. and Pöhlmann, S. (1990) A Methodology for Uncertainty in Knowledge-Based Systems; Lecture Notes in Artificial Intelligence, Vol. 419, Springer.

Wensley, A. (1989) Research Directions in Expert Systems; in Knowledge-Based Management Support Systems, eds. Georgios I. Doukidis, Frank Land, Gordon Miller; Ellis Horwood, Chichester.

5 Are there any lessons to be learnt from the building of GLIMPSE?

C. M. O'Brien
Statistical Computing Consultant,
University of London Computer Centre

GLIMPSE is a knowledge-based front-end for the statistical package GLIM 3.77. It provides a user with assistance and optional guidance in the application of generalised linear modelling techniques to statistical data sets. It is intended to increase a user's understanding of generalised linear modelling and facilitate the use of suitable statistical techniques.

This paper addresses the strengths and weaknesses inherent in the knowledge-based front-end approach to statistical software design and elucidates the lessons learnt from the building of the first commercial statistical knowledge-based front-end system, GLIMPSE.

The future for statistical software design and provision is an uncertain one. Mistakes made now will be costly in the future.

Keywords: decision support tool, front-end system, generalised linear model, knowledge-based system, statistics.

1   INTRODUCTION

There are many useful, powerful, tried and tested software packages in existence but few offer users advice either on how they may be used or on how they should be used. The statistical packages of the present time are, by and large, non-conversational and an analyst programmer must know what to do; i.e. which statistical techniques are appropriate for which data structures, and how to carry them out via the command language of the package.

Front-ends to software packages are designed principally to make the packages easier to use and to extend the facilities provided by the package. Knowledge-based front-ends (KBFEs) are essentially front-ends that contain explicitly represented knowledge of the back-end package; i.e. of the syntax and semantics of the command language, and of the domain in which the system may be used in general and on how it may be used efficiently and sensibly in a particular situation. Section 2 of this paper discusses the development of a front-end system to the interactive GLIM 3.77 statistics package (Payne, 1985) that can provide such advice.

The front-end, GLIMPSE (Generalised Linear Interactive Modelling with PROLOG and Statistical Expertise), is the result of a collaborative project whose primary objectives were to investigate the feasibility of using logic programming techniques and tools, modified and extended as necessary, in the development of front-ends to large software packages (O'Brien, 1986). It was developed jointly by the Departments of Computing and Mathematics at Imperial College of Science, Technology & Medicine, London and the Numerical Algorithms Group Limited, Oxford under the UK Government Alvey programme (contract ALV/PRJ/IKBS/033). The front-end is written entirely in a dialect of PROLOG and uses the augmented PROLOG system, APES developed by Hammond and Sergot (1984), as the basis of its inference mechanism; APES also provides declarative dialogue and explanation facilities. Some extensions to APES were necessary and a new interpreter (Wolstenholme and O'Brien, 1987) was adapted.

2   A KBFE FOR GLIM 3.77

Work on the development of a prototype GLIMPSE system began during October 1984 and ceased at the end of September 1987; after which time the production of a marketable product was actively pursued by the Numerical Algorithms Group Limited, Oxford.

The principal requirements of such a front-end were:

(a) those of a traditional front-end

- it should make the existing facilities of GLIM easier to use;
- it should enhance the facilities provided by GLIM.

(b) those of a knowledge-based front-end

- it should give advice on what actions to undertake during a statistical analysis;
- it should give advice on interpreting the output from the system; i.e. on what conclusions may be reached, based on broadly established principles.

Certain constraints and requirements were placed upon the front-end:

(a) the advice given should be non-authoritarian

- the user should be free to reject the advice given and to follow a different approach from that suggested by the knowledge-based front-end;

(b) the system should be able to explain, in some way, any advice given;

(c) there should be several modes of use for a range of users, including
- those who wish to ask for advice and let the system carry out the action advised;
- those who do not wish to ask for advice, but wish to instigate actions directly, with only occasional guidance;

(d) the system should provide clarification of questions or terms used.

Full details of the development and building of GLIMPSE are to be found in Wolstenholme et al. (1988) and O'Brien (1990).

The benefits of the KBFE approach to software design are that analyses can take hours to accomplish rather than the days or weeks needed when using the back-end software package directly. The analyst may concentrate on 'what do I want to do?' rather than 'how do I program?'. However, there are drawbacks! KBFEs have limited knowledge domains, are not easily amenable to adaptation and can be restrictive; suppressing freedom of choice within a less than flexible structure.

3   A PERSONAL PERSPECTIVE ON STATISTICAL COMPUTING

When undertaking a statistical analysis, an analyst aims to discover enough facts about a data set to make certain inferences; e.g. to decide that one or more statistical model adequately describes the data. In computerised analysis, for example, the analyst may use the calculation and graphics facilities of a statistics package to explore the data and gain further insight into their properties and pattern. The process is by no means linear, as some results may seduce the analyst into following a path that leads nowhere. The analyst then has to backtrack and try a different path. However, results found along the unsuccessful path are not necessarily wasted, and may prove useful later.

Tools at the disposal of the computational statistician and mathematical analyst to help in this process are many and varied. These comprise:

- the programming language (such as FORTRAN);
- the statistical software package (such as BMDP and SAS);
- the decision support tool (such as directed graph approaches to the selection of a solution);
- the front-end system (such as SENAC (Punjani and Broughan, 1990));
- the knowledge-based system (such as GLIMPSE);

and, more recently,

- the environment for statistical computing (such as S-PLUS (Becker et al., 1988)).

In the case of the knowledge-based system GLIMPSE, the underlying programming language for statistical computation is FORTRAN 77, the statistical software package based on this programming language is GLIM 3.77 and the front-end system to this software package is written in sigma-PROLOG (McCabe et al., 1984) and APES.

Considering the linear transition from the programming language to the knowledge-based system one may make a number of observations. Firstly, the ease of use changes from 'low' (for the programming language) to 'high' (for the knowledge-based system) as one progresses down the list. However, the degree of flexibility changes from 'high' (for the programming language) to 'low' (for the knowledge-based system). To illustrate, consider the following problem posed to me in a recent consultation at the University of London Computer Centre by a user of the Amdahl 5890/300.

One has two datasets. Let the first be denoted A and the second denoted B. Sort the variables in the two datasets on the basis of a variable 'case code' representing a unique numeric code for each observation in each dataset. Compare each 'case code' in the dataset A with each 'case code' in the dataset B. If there is a match, combine the variables in the two datasets by 'case code'. How may this be achieved? A number of alternative solutions are possible:

- The solution with a programming language such as FORTRAN is tedious and will involve array-indexing within nested do-loops.
- The solution with a statistical software package such as SAS is comparatively easy. Let the 'case code' variable be denoted by INDIC in both the datasets. Then the code

    DATA C;
       MERGE A (IN=QQ) B (IN=Q)
       BY INDIC;
       IF Q AND QQ;

    will produce the desired result.
- The solution with a knowledge-based system such as GLIMPSE is trivial. Let the 'case code' variable be denoted by INDICA in the dataset A and be denoted by INDICB in the dataset B. Then the code

    SUBSET COMBINE (INDICA ON INDICB)

    will produce the desired result.

The first solution approach has a high degree of flexibility, the third a low degree; the first solution approach is tedious, the third is merely trivial.

The historical development of computational statistical software along the parallel routes:

   − programming language to statistical software package,

- statistical software package to front-end system,
- front-end system to knowledge-based system,

seems natural and followed from a desire to eliminate the complexities sometimes inherent in computer-based analyses. However, such developments typically result in less than optimal software design and provision. The routes:

- programming language to statistical specification system,
- statistical specification system to environment for statistical computing,

are preferable to my mind and such a path will form the basis of the later section 8.

Consider the historical development of software along the parallel paths. section 4 discusses the progression from the programming language/package to decision support tool, while section 5 is concerned with the transition from decision support tool to front-end system. In section 6 the transition from front-end system to knowledge-based system is discussed and in section 7 the progression to an environment for statistical computing is discussed. Finally, in section 8 a possible future for software design and provision will be discussed.

4   PROGRAMMING LANGUAGE/PACKAGE TO DECISION SUPPORT TOOL

Two of the earliest aids to computation were the programming language and the software package.

Both the programming language and the statistical software package offer the computational statistician and mathematical analyst a high degree of flexibility but at the expense of ease of use. To help make the use of such software systems less tedious, decision support tools were developed. Essentially, menu-driven and easily programmable in, for example, both PROLOG and APES these are designed to help the user to write computer code. Consider the application of non-parametric correlation in the context of the Mark 13 NAG FORTRAN library.

A number of distinct question-and-answer routes are possible to decide upon the appropriate subroutine to use from the library:

PATH ONE:

    question - are there any missing values?

      answer - no

    question - can input data be overwritten to save time?

      answer - no

---

    recommend NAG FORTRAN library subroutine G02BQF

PATH TWO:

> question - are there any missing values?
> answer - no
> question - can input data be overwritten to save time?
> answer - yes

---

recommend NAG FORTRAN library subroutine G02BNF

PATH THREE:

> question - are there any missing values?
> answer - yes
> question - are missing values to be omitted casewise?
> answer - no

---

recommend NAG FORTRAN library subroutine G02BSF

PATH FOUR:

> question - are there any missing values?
> answer - yes
> question - are missing values to be omitted casewise?
> answer - yes
> question - can input data array be overwritten to save time?
> answer - no

---

recommend NAG FORTRAN library subroutine G02BRF

PATH FIVE:

> question - are there any missing values?
> answer - yes
> question - are missing values to be omitted casewise?
> answer - yes
> question - can input data array be overwritten to save time?
> answer - yes

---

recommend NAG FORTRAN library subroutine G02BPF

The question-and-answer dialogue may be routinely programmed. However, while any such derived decision tools may recommend the subroutine algorithm most appropriate for the application they do not produce a computer program to solve the problem. They merely make a recommendation and leave the task of incorporating the algorithm into a program to the user. In an effort to overcome this obvious deficiency, front-end systems were developed.

5   DECISION SUPPORT TOOL TO FRONT-END SYSTEM

Front-ends to software packages are designed principally to make the packages easier to use and to extend the facilities provided by the package. They may be used to tailor a package originally designed for general use to a particular class of user.

Front-ends have an important commercial role to play since they can extend the working life of an existing piece of software. The advantage of using a front-end instead of developing a new version of the software is that the debugging and improvements made over the years are not wasted; the system can be used as a stable item with familiar features. Consider a front-end system to the Mark 13 NAG FORTRAN library.

SENAC (Symbolic Environment for Numerical and Algebraic Computation) is an easy-to-use interface to the NAG FORTRAN and Graphics libraries. It makes available all the advantages of NAG library routines – their efficiency, accuracy and robustness – allowing users to solve problems quickly and easily, avoiding the complexities of large-scale FORTRAN programming.

SENAC is not interpretive. When a NAG library routine is used, SENAC generates, compiles and links FORTRAN code to use the routine. If user-defined programs are required, SENAC converts them from symbolic form into FORTRAN. If the NAG routine requires derivatives, SENAC forms symbolic derivatives and codes them into FORTRAN as well.

This process takes place unseen to the user. The FORTRAN code produced by SENAC is linked in the background and executed automatically. The output is caught and returned to SENAC for immediate use. The essential feature is that computation is carried out by optimised compiled code. SENAC is ideal for prototyping numerical algorithms. However, there are drawbacks!

Front-ends, such as SENAC, require the user to be a domain 'expert'; i.e. if one has a problem which requires the solution to an integral equation then one must be aware of this fact before attempting to use the front-end and back-end systems. In an effort to overcome this obvious deficiency, knowledge-based front-ends were developed.

6   FRONT-END SYSTEM TO KNOWLEDGE-BASED SYSTEM

KBFEs are essentially front-ends that contain explicitly represented knowledge of the back-end package; i.e. of the syntax and semantics of the command language, and of the domain in which the system is to be used. They can therefore advise the user on how the system may be used in general and on how it may be used efficiently and sensibly in a particular situation. They may also contain explicit knowledge of the user or users. KBFEs permit users to interact with the system using a language familiar to them rather than the language of the back-end. A general discussion of such front-ends is given by Bundy (1984).

There are currently only a limited number of KBFEs in existence. Most of these are still prototypes or in use only for research purposes. In most such systems the conceptual distance between the user input language and the package is minimal, and in general there is no task specification. However, more recent KBFE projects have extended the conceptual distance between the user and the back-end. The early systems, generally based on projection rules (see, for example, Johnson and Keravnou (1985, section 1.2.4)), greatly influenced later researchers, including those working in logic. Chief amongst these, judging by the number of times they are referenced, are MYCIN and its direct descendants (Buchanan and Shortliffe, 1984).

Besides the benefits of a knowledge-based system discussed elsewhere in this paper there are drawbacks. KBFEs have limited knowledge domains, are not adaptable and are restrictive. In an effort to overcome these deficiencies, environments for statistical computing were developed.

7   KNOWLEDGE-BASED SYSTEM TO ENVIRONMENT FOR STATISTICAL COMPUTING

Environments for statistical computing provide an interactive environment for computing, permit graphical data analysis, provide a quantitative programming language, and are extensible. Consider one such system, S-PLUS.

S-PLUS is an interactive computing environment designed explicitly for interactive graphics workstations which includes both a graphical data analysis system and an advanced quantitative programming language. It is a system for the production of graphics, exploratory data analysis, statistics and mathematical computing. Its flexible quantitative programming environment and powerful system of analytical tools makes it ideal for prototyping numerical algorithms – from the simplest to the most sophisticated applications. Refer to Therneau (1990) for a review of S-PLUS and a comparison with SAS.

8   THE FUTURE

Work on the knowledge-based system GLIMPSE has identified areas in which further fundamental research is required. This research, as outlined below, may result in further development effort being required:

- Current rule-based explanations of how an answer was found, which are given in a top-down fashion, can be very tedious. Research is required into improving such rule-based explanations and/or replacing them with non-rule-based explanations.
- A user of GLIMPSE is able to customise aspects of the environment/interface in several ways. However, GLIMPSE is not an adaptive interface except for the fact that once guidance is requested to a question, the system assumes that the user will always need guidance with this question. Research into the development of an adaptive interface needs to be undertaken.

The solutions to these and other related topics may, ultimately, allow one to experiment with front-ends based on three simple ideas:

1. a user can immediately declare levels of expertise in the use of a back-end package and statistical knowledge, for instance, so that the system automatically employs a number of ready-made front-ends;

2. the system can monitor its dialogue with the user, alter its view of the user dynamically and respond accordingly by modifying the front-end;

3. the user may benefit from a front-end which,when the system fails to perform a desired task, can direct the user along related and potentially fruitful paths.

Any front-end must, of course, be non-authoritarian and be able to justify to a user any of its suggested actions during the course of an analysis. However, are such developments REALLY necessary? Who are the systems being developed for? Do they want the systems? Will they use the systems? The list of questions is endless.

Personally, I regard the impracticality of developing general knowledge-based statistical computing systems for the statistician, as opposed to limited-domain systems for non-statisticians working in particular subject areas, as a handicap which may not be overcome. The future for statistical computing lies with environments for statistical computation!

Future systems must have a user interface incorporating state-of-the-art technologies corresponding to the WIMPs of today, an interface with a database, the ability to check input restrictions, and links with numerical software libraries. The development of any such systems will require close collaboration between technical statisticians, computer scientists and data experts.

REFERENCES

Becker, R.A., Chambers, J.M. and Wilks, A.R. (1988) The New S Language. Wadsworth: Belmont, CA.

Buchanan, B.G. and Shortliffe, E.H. (eds.) (1984) Rule-Based Expert Systems: The MYCIN Experiments of the Stanford Heuristic Programming Project. Addison-Wesley: Reading, Massachusetts.

Bundy, A. (1984) Intelligent front ends. Research Paper No. 227, Department of Artificial Intelligence, University of Edinburgh.

Hammond, P. and Sergot, M.J. (1984) APES: Augmented PROLOG for Expert Systems, Reference Manual. Logic Based Systems Ltd: Surrey.

Johnson, L. and Keravnou, E.T. (1985) Expert Systems Technology: A Guide. Abacus Press: Cambridge, Massachusetts.

McCabe, F.G., Clark, K.L., Steel, B.D. and French, P.D. (1984) sigma-PROLOG 1.0 Programmer's Reference Manual. Logic Programming Associates Ltd: London.

O'Brien, C. (1986) One view of the GLIM/IKBS initiative (GLIMPSE). GLIM Newsletter No. 12, pp. 5–13.

O'Brien, C.M. (1990) The GLIMPSE System Compendium. Unpublished manuscript.

Payne, C.D. (ed.) (1985) The GLIM System, Release 3.77, Generalised Linear Interactive Modelling Manual. Numerical Algorithms Group Ltd: Oxford.

Punjani, M. and Broughan, K.A. (eds.) (1990) SENAC – Computer based algebra and NAG. ULCC News, No. 247, pp. 12–15.

Therneau, T.M. (1990) S-PLUS. The American Statistician, Vol. 44, pp. 239–241.

Wolstenholme, D.E. and O'Brien, C.M. (1987) GLIMPSE – a statistical adventure. Proceedings of the 10th International Joint Conference on Artificial Intelligence (IJCAI 87, Milan, 23-28 August 1987), Vol. 1, pp. 596–599.

Wolstenholme, D.E., O'Brien, C.M. and Nelder, J.A. (1988) GLIMPSE: a knowledge-based front end for statistical analysis. Knowledge-Based Systems, Vol. 1, pp. 173–178.

6 Handling imprecisely-known conditional probabilities

S. Amarger, D. Dubois and H. Prade
IRIT, Toulouse, France

1 INTRODUCTION

In commonsense reasoning it is often necessary to manipulate rules with exceptions. One of the most important cases of such rules consists in default statements containing explicit or implicit numerical quantifiers. Even when they are explicit these quantifiers may be only vaguely stated as for instance "most students are young" (see [Zadeh85]). The numerical approach interprets the linguistic term "most" as an ill-defined numerical quantifier expressing the proportion of young people among students, in a certain context. More generally, we may have some statement about the value of the probability of not encountering an exception, i.e. in our example the conditional probability P(young | student), which expresses a degree of certainty that a student taken at random is indeed young (for simplicity we assume here that 'young' has a clear-cut meaning and is not viewed as a fuzzy predicate; see [Dubois88] for preliminary results on the handling of fuzzy predicates in this framework.

Different kinds of treatment can be imagined for rules of the kind "if A then B with probability P(B | A)". This can be illustrated considering the above rule and another which can be chained with it, namely, "if B then C with probability P(C | B)". Applying Bayes' rule we have $P(C | A) \geq P(B \cap C | A) = P(C | A \cap B)P(B | A)$ (here we use the same symbol '$\cap$' for denoting the conjunction of propositions or the intersection of the classes of items which satisfy the propositions). Then assuming irrelevance of A with respect to C in the context B, namely assuming here that $P(C | A \cap B) = P(C | B)$, we obtain the lower bound $P(C | B)P(B | A)$ for $P(C | A)$. But without this kind of assumption, as soon as $P(C | B) \neq 1$, nothing can be said about the value of $P(C | A)$ which can take any value in the interval [0,1]. Indeed nothing forbids to have $A \cap C = \emptyset$ (leading to $P(C | A) = 0$) as well as $A \subseteq C$ (leading to $P(C | A) = 1$) for instance. Interestingly enough if we add some information about $P(A | B)$ we may obtain non-trivial bounds for $P(C | A)$ just from bounds on $P(B | A)$, $P(A | B)$ and $P(C | B)$; see section 5. Then more generally we may choose either (i) to exploit the available knowledge on conditional probabilities for computing the best possible upper and lower bounds for some other conditional probabilities of interest, or (ii) to take advantage of independence assumptions (which are perhaps hard to check) for computing probability estimates. The first approach may give no informative result, but when results are informative, they are very strong. On the contrary, the Bayesian approach always gives informative results, but these results can always be questioned by the arrival of new pieces of information. In this paper we investigate the first approach in detail.

Formally, let X be a set of objects, A and B be two subsets of X, and Q_B^A be a subset of values (which may reduce to a single value) expressing what is known about the proportion of A's which are B's. Q_B^A is a sub-interval of the unit interval [0,1], corresponding to the default rule "Q_B^A A's are B's". This knowledge is understood as a constraint acting on the cardinality of B relative to A, i.e.:

$$\frac{|A \cap B|}{|A|} \in Q_B^A \subseteq [0, 1]$$

where |A| is the cardinality of the subset A. More generally, it is equivalent to a piece of information of the form $P(B \mid A) \in [P_*(B \mid A), P^*(B \mid A)]$ where only the two bounds $P_*(B \mid A)$ and $P^*(B \mid A)$ are known. Indeed relative cardinality is a particular case of conditional probability, where the underlying distribution is uniformly distributed over X. Thus proportions and probabilities obey the same mathematical laws and we shall use them in an interchangeable way in the following. We use a network representation, as for instance the one on Figure 1, where the two directed edges between two nodes A and B are weighted by Q_A^B and Q_B^A, i.e. what is known of the proportions of B's which are A's and of A's which are B's. Note that in terms of conditional probabilities we assume information on both $P(A \mid B)$ and $P(B \mid A)$, which contrasts with Bayesian networks ([Pearl88]). Besides $P(A)$ will be interpreted as $P(A \mid X)$ where X stands for the set of all considered objects or in logical terms corresponds to the ever-true proposition. Hence all probabilities that we handle are (bounds of) conditional probabilities in a network where cycles are allowed, and no prior probability information is required in order to start the inference process in the approach described in this paper.

In the following sections, we are going to introduce the different patterns used to reason with such networks and the techniques that can handle the underlying imprecisely-known conditional probabilities. This work is the continuation of several pieces of work. In [Dubois88] (see also [LéaSombé90]), a first local pattern of reasoning, corresponding to the transitive chaining syllogism was studied. In [Dubois90] two other local patterns enable to estimate conditional probabilities involving conjunctions of events or contexts in their expression. Besides [Amarger90] and [van der Gaag90a] have proposed a global computation method, which is based on the reduction to a linear programming problem, of the optimisation problem generated by the set of constraints corresponding to the available information on conditional probabilities and where we look for the best lower and upper bounds of the conditional probability to estimate. In the next section we state the problem which we are dealing with in more precise terms and define the notions of soundness and completeness in this framework. In section 3, it is recalled how our problem can be reduced to linear programming. Section 4 presents a generalised version of Bayes' theorem which can help improve the known bounds using an inference network in a single propagation step. Sections 5 and 6 recall the previously studied patterns. Section 7 introduces new patterns involving disjunctions. Section 8 discusses the handling of negation. Section 9 presents the general strategy for using local patterns in order to answer queries about conditional probabilities of interest. Section 10 discusses the handling of conjunction and disjunction in queries. Section 11 illustrates the approach in an example.

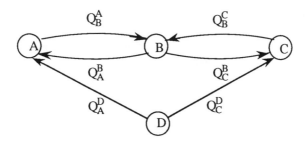

Figure 1 An inference network.

2   STATEMENT OF THE PROBLEM

We suppose that we know some default rules containing numerical quantifiers or conditional probabilities such as "Q_B^A A's are B's" or "if A then B with probability P(B | A)."

Our objective in this paper is to answer queries like: "what proportion of A's are C's?", "what proportion of A's and B's are C's?", "what proportion of C's are A's and B's?", "what proportion of A's or B's are C's?", or "what proportion of C's are A's or B's?"; or similar queries stated in terms of conditional probabilities, from the available knowledge about the values of other proportions or conditional probabilities. This corresponds respectively to evaluate the probabilities $p = P(C \mid A)$, $P(C \mid A \cap B)$, $P(A \cap B \mid C)$, $P(C \mid A \cup B)$ or $P(A \cup B \mid C)$. The possible values of p usually form an interval $[p_*, p^*]$, and not just a single value, where p_* is the lowest value and p^* the highest value taken by the conditional probability.

As far as the evaluation of p means the computation of a lower and an upper bound, we have to consider two important potential properties of the computation procedure:

- **soundness:** a method which treats numerical quantifiers must provide sound results, i.e. if $\hat{p}_*$ and $\hat{p}^*$ are the best bounds, and p_* and p^* are the bounds supplied by the method, we must have: $p_* \le \hat{p}_*$ and $\hat{p}^* \le p^*$ which is equivalent to $[\hat{p}_*, \hat{p}^*] \subseteq [p_*, p^*]$.
- **completeness:** a method provides complete results when $p_* = \hat{p}_*$ and $p^* = \hat{p}^*$. This latter property is important from a theoretical point of view, but in practice if the differences between the actual greatest lower and least upper bounds and the computed bounds are small, the numerical quantifier can be considered as properly estimated.

The patterns we propose in the following sections are sound and are also complete when we consider just the elementary network corresponding to the statement of the pattern, i.e. they are said to be locally complete. Graphically, to answer a query like "what proportion of X's are Y's?" is equivalent to generate the new edge <X,Y> in a network like the one of Figure 1. Our approach is local in the sense that the patterns are designed to provide answers to particular queries using local inference rules. Consequently, one can observe the influence of each piece of knowledge on the result; global methods do not offer such a possibility. Even though a particular pattern corresponds to an elementary network, the inference patterns can work on any network, whatever its structure, unlike the Bayesian approach which needs an acyclic network topology (e.g. directed cycles are prohibited) adapted to the propagation mechanism (see [Lauritzen88] and [Pearl88]). Of course, in practice, in order to answer a particular query, several possibilities may exist for applying the patterns to the network, corresponding to different paths. When the inference rules are sound, one can easily combine the different results provided by all the applications of patterns because their intersection still provides a sound result. Indeed, let us suppose that $Q_1 = [p_{*1}, p^*_1]$ and $Q_2 = [p_{*2}, p^*_2]$ are two intervals that contain the value p we want to estimate; then we have: $p \in Q_1 \cap Q_2 = [\max(p_{*1}, p_{*2}), \min(p^*_1, p^*_2)]$. This generalises to the intersection of any number of intervals; and the emptiness of the intersection would be the proof that the data we start with are not consistent.

3 THE GLOBAL METHOD

It has been shown in [Paass88] and in [Besnard90] that reasoning from such numerically quantified general rules may be modelled as an optimisation problem.

For instance, if we take the example of the three following classes (Student, Young, Single), then, $8 = 2^3$ elementary classes should be considered, corresponding respectively to Student $\cap$ Young $\cap$ Single, $\neg$Student $\cap$ Young $\cap$ Single, Student $\cap$ $\neg$Young $\cap$ Single, and so on, where $\neg$A denotes the complement of class A, or, equivalently, the negation of proposition A. Let us denote by $x_{St, Yg, Si}$, where St, Yg, Si $\in$ {0, 1}, the eight corresponding variables. For instance, $x_{0, 0, 1}$ represents the proportion of non-students which are not-young but single. In this case, $x_{St, Yg, Si} \in [0,1]$ and

$$\sum_{St, Yg, Si \in [0, 1]} x_{St, Yg, Si} = 1.$$

We have then:

$$|Student| = x_{1, 1, 1} + x_{1, 0, 1} + x_{1, 0, 0}$$

and

$$|Student \cap Young| = x_{1, 1, 0} + x_{1, 1, 1} \; ; \; etc.$$

So, the piece of information "Q_{Yg}^{St} Student are Young" gives birth to the two linear constraints, with $Q_{Yg}^{St} = [p1_*, p1^*]$:

$$x_{1, 1, 0} + x_{1, 1, 1} \leq p1_* (x_{1, 1, 1} + x_{1, 0, 1} + x_{1, 1, 0} + x_{1, 0 0})$$

$$(L_1)$$

$$x_{1, 1, 0} + x_{1, 1, 1} \geq p1^* (x_{1, 1, 1} + x_{1, 0, 1} + x_{1, 1, 0} + x_{1, 0, 0})$$

Let $\mathcal{l}$ be the set of linear constraints, obtained by translating the available information, e.g. $L_1 \in \mathcal{l}$. Then, what is known of the proportion of students which are single, for instance, will be given by:

$$p_* = \inf \left\{ \frac{x_{1, 0, 1} + x_{1, 1, 1}}{x_{1, 1, 1} + x_{1, 0, 1} + x_{1, 1, 0} + x_{1, 0, 0}} \; under \; \mathcal{L} \right\}$$

$$p^* = \sup \left\{ \frac{x_{1, 0, 1} + x_{1, 1, 1}}{x_{1, 1, 1} + x_{1, 0, 1} + x_{1, 1, 0} + x_{1, 0, 0}} \; under \; \mathcal{L} \right\}$$

As we can see we are faced with a fractional linear programming problem ([Charnes62]). The same approach may be used to solve any query and can be found, in terms of probabilities, in [Paass88] where a "scanning" method is proposed for solving the mathematical programming problem.

Linear fractional programs of the form (P),

$$(P) \begin{cases} \text{Opti} \dfrac{c \cdot {}^t x}{d \cdot {}^t x}, \ x \geq 0 \\ 1 \cdot {}^t x \ = \ 1 \\ B \cdot x \ \leq \ 0 \end{cases}$$

where 1 is the "unit vector," c, d, x are row vectors, B is matrix, "Opti". is either "Max" or "Min", and t denotes the transposition, can be transformed into an equivalent linear program (P'). Indeed, as pointed out in [Charnes62] (see also [Schaible83]), letting $y_i = x_i /((d \cdot {}^t x)$, we obtain:

$$(P') \begin{cases} \text{Opti } c \cdot {}^t y, \ y \geq 0 \\ d \cdot {}^t y \ = \ 1 \\ B \cdot y \ \leq \ 0 \end{cases}$$

So, as explained and exemplified in [Amarger90], we have to solve two linear programs (one to compute the exact lower bound and one to compute the exact upper bound). But, even if with this method we are able to precisely compute the best bounds bracketing the conditional probability of interest, it would be hard to try to explain the obtained results in terms of the available knowledge we start with, as already said.

This reduction of a fractional linear programming problem induced by probability constraints to a linear programming problem has been also pointed out and used in [van der Gaag90a], where also local computation methods are proposed on the basis of the decomposition of the linear system in subsystems, and exploiting independence relationships when they are known (see [van der Gaag90b]).

Methods based on local inference patterns may provide less precise results (although they are guaranteed to be sound), but which are easier to explain. Before presenting the basic inference patterns, we now give a generalisation of the Bayes' theorem.

4   GENERALISED BAYES' THEOREM

In the framework of numerical quantifiers, because we manipulate conditional probabilities, it would be interesting to use the Bayes' theorem:

$$\forall A, B \quad P(A \mid B) = P(B \mid A) \cdot P(A)/P(B)$$

But, in our approach we do not assume that $P(A)$ and $P(B)$ are known. A more general identity, where only conditional probabilities appear can be established:

Theorem 1: Generalised Bayes' theorem

$$\forall A_1, ..., A_n \quad P(A_1 \mid A_n) = P(A_n \mid A_1) \prod_{i=1}^{n-1} \frac{P(A_i \mid A_{i+1})}{P(A_{i+1} \mid A_i)}$$

when all involved quantities are positive.

This identity is easily proved by replacing conditional probabilities $P(A \mid B)$ by their expressions $P(A \cap B)/P(B)$. Note that this identity tells us that given a cycle $A_1, A_2, ..., A_n, A_{n+1} = A_1$ in a probabilistic network, the $2.n$ quantities $\{P(A_i \mid A_{i+1}), i = 1, n\} \cup \{P(A_{i+1} \mid A_i), i = 1, n\}$ are not independent when positive: any $2.n - 1$ of these quantities determine the remaining one. Now, because we use upper and lower probabilities, we extend this theorem as follows[1]:

Theorem 2: Generalised Bayes' theorem – upper/lower probabilities case
- lower bound:

$$\forall A_1, ..., A_n \quad P_*(A_1 \mid A_n) \geq P_*(A_n \mid A_1) \prod_{i=1}^{n-1} d_{i,i+1}$$

with: $\forall i, j \in \;]n]$, $d_{i,j} = P_*(A_iA_j)/P_*(A_jA_i)$, for $n > 2$
- upper bound:

$$\forall A_1, ..., A_n \quad P^*(A_1 \mid A_n) \leq P^*(A_n \mid A_1) \prod_{i=1}^{n-1} \overline{d}_{i,i+1}$$

with: $\forall i, j \in \;]n]$, $\overline{d}_{i,j} = P^*(A_i \mid A_j)/P^*(A_j \mid A_i)$, for $n > 2$

---

1   Notation: $]n] \equiv \;]0,n] \cap N$.

Let N be the probabilistic network defined by the 4-uples $(\Omega, U, \underline{P}, \overline{P})$, where:

Ω is the set of the nodes of the network, with $|\Omega| = \omega$,
U the incidence matrix,
$\underline{P}$ the lower probabilities matrix: $\forall i, j \in]\omega]$, $\underline{P}_{i,j} = P_*(A_i \mid A_j)$
$\overline{P}$ the upper probabilities matrix: $\forall i, j \in]\omega]$, $\overline{P}_{i,j} = P^*(A_i \mid A_j)$

We define two new networks as follows:

$N = (\Omega, U, \underline{L})$ and

$\overline{N} = (\Omega, U, \overline{L})$,

where: $\forall i, j \in]\omega]$, $\underline{L}_{i,j} = \underline{d}_{i,j}$ and $\overline{L}_{i,j} = \overline{d}_{i,j}$.

We have to notice that: $\forall i, j \in]\omega]$, $\underline{d}_{i,j} = 1/\underline{d}_{j,i}$ so: $\underline{L} = ({}^{t}\underline{L})^{(-1)}$

The calculation of $P_*(A_1 \mid A_n)$ thus comes down to the computation of

$\underline{\delta}_{1n} = \prod_{i=1}^{n-1} \underline{d}_{i,i+1}$, over all paths in $\underline{N}$, going from A_1 to A_n, in a non-direct way,

and to take the greatest among such values. Similarly, the calculation of $P^*(A_1 \mid A_n)$ requires the computation of the smallest $\overline{\delta}_{n1} = \prod_{i=1}^{n-1} \overline{d}_{i,i+1}$, among all non-direct paths going from A_1 to A_n in $\overline{N}$. We need non-direct paths because Theorem 2 does not hold for $n = 2$, i.e. we cannot take into account the weights $\underline{d}_{1,n}$ and $\underline{d}_{n,1}$ when computing $P_*(A_1 \mid A_n)$ and $\underline{P}_*(A_1 \mid A_n)$. Due to the above noticed duality relation between matrices $\underline{L}$ and $\overline{L}$, δ_{n1} corresponds to the longest path from A_n to A_1 in $\underline{N}$ when arc $(n, 1)$ has been deleted. Hence, only one of $\underline{N}$ and $\overline{N}$ need to be stored. In other words:

Proposition 1:
• to compute $P_*(A_1 \mid A_n)$, it is enough to find a longest[1] non-direct path between A_1 and A_n in $\underline{N}$ over the dioid[2] $(\Re \cup \{+\infty\}, \max, \times)$.
The length of this path is $\underline{\delta}_{1n}$. Then $P_*(A_1 \mid A_n) = P_*(A_n \mid A_1).\underline{\delta}_{1n}$

---

1   I.e. most weighted.
2   Also called a semi-ring in [Gondran85].

- to compute $P^*(A_1 \mid A_n)$ it is enough to find a longest non-direct path between A_n and A_1 in $\underline{N}$ over the dioid $(\Re \cup \{+\infty\}, \max, \times)$. The length of this path is $\underline{\delta}_{m1}$. Then $P^*(A_1 \mid A_n) = P^*(A_n \mid A_1) / \underline{\delta}_{n1}$.

Here, the length of a path is the product of the (positive) weights of its arcs. From a computational point of view, it is easier to define the new following network: $\underline{Log\ N} = (\Omega, U, \underline{Log\ L})$ where: $\forall i, j \in]\omega], \underline{Log\ L}_{i,j} = Log\ (\underline{d}_{i,j})$.

Then, we come down to usual path algebras, namely:

Proposition 2:
- to compute $Log(P_*(A_1 \mid A_n))$ is equivalent to find a longest non-direct path between A_1 and A_n in $\underline{Log\ N}$ over the dioid $(\Re \cup \{+\infty\}, \max, \times)$.
- to compute $Log(P^*(A_1 \mid A_n))$ is equivalent to determine a longest non-direct path between A_n and A_1 in $\underline{Log\ N}$ over the dioid $(\Re \cup \{+\infty\}, \max, \times)$.

And, a longest path always exists between two nodes of $\underline{Log\ N}$, because there is no positive weight circuit in $\underline{Log\ N}$ (see proof in Annex 3).

5   TRANSITIVE CHAINING

The first local inference pattern, already examined in [Dubois88] and in [Dubois90], corresponds to the evaluation of a missing edge in the inference network (see Figure 2).

We first suppose that the available proportions (or, equivalently, conditional probabilities) are precisely known; then we propose generalised formulas that handle the case where their values are only known to belong to intervals. In any case answering a query corresponds to compute a lower bound p* and an upper bound p* which define an interval that contains all the possible values of the probability p that we want to determine.

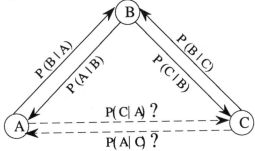

Figure 2   Pattern I.

Since this scheme is symmetrical, we only evaluate the proportion $|(A \cap C)| / |A|$, or, more generally, the probability $P(C \mid A) = P(C \cap A)/P(A)$, of the A's which are C's. The value of the following quantities is supposed to be known: $P(B \mid A)$, $P(A \mid B)$, $P(C \mid B)$ and $P(B \mid C)$. We want to determine $P(C \mid A)$. In fact, we can only determine the greatest lower bound, $P_*(C \mid A)$, and, the least upper bound, $P^*(C \mid A)$, with respect to the information provided by the four above-mentioned probabilities, where $P(C \mid A) \in [(P_*(C \mid A), P^*(C \mid A)]$.

5.1   For the Lower Bound:

Taking advantage of the inequality $\max(0, P(A \cap B) + P(B \cap C) - P(B)) \leq P(A \cap C)$, it can be proved that ([Dubois88], [Dubois90]):

$$P_* (C \mid A) = \frac{P(B \mid A)}{P(A \mid B)} \max\, 0, P(A \mid B) + P(C \mid B) - 1) \tag{1}$$

(1) easily extends to the case of imprecisely-known conditional probabilities as follows:

$$P_* (C \mid A) = P_* (B \mid A) \max \left(0,1 - \frac{1 - P_* (C \mid B)}{P_* (A \mid B)} \right) \tag{2}$$

5.2   For the Upper Bound:

From the four following inequalities,

$$P(A \cap C) \leq P(A); \ P(A \cap C) \leq P(A) - P(A \cap B) + P(B \cap C)$$
$$P(A \cap C) \leq P(C); \ P(A \cap C) \leq P(C) + P(A \cap B) - P(B \cap C)$$

we derive the following upper bound which can be proved to be the least one ([Dubois88], [Dubois90]):

$$P^*(C \mid A) = \min \left(1, \ 1 - P(B \mid A) + \frac{P(B \mid A) . P(C \mid B)}{P(A \mid B)}, \ \frac{P(B \mid A) . P(C \mid B)}{P(A \mid B) . P(B \mid C)}, \right.$$

$$\left. \frac{P(B \mid A) . P(C \mid B)}{P(A \mid B) . P(B \mid C)} [\, 1 - P(B \mid C)\,] + P(B \mid A) \right) \tag{3}$$

(3) is extended to imprecisely-known conditional probabilities as follows:

$$P^* (C \mid A) =$$

$$\min \left(1, \ 1 - P_* (B \mid A) + \frac{P_* (B \mid A) \cdot P^* (C \mid B)}{P_* (A \mid B)}, \ \frac{P^* (B \mid A) \cdot P^* (C \mid B)}{P_* (A \mid B) \cdot P_* (B \mid C)}, \right.$$

$$\left. \frac{P^* (B \mid A) \cdot P^* (C \mid B)}{P_* (A \mid B) \cdot P_* (B \mid C)} [1 - P_* (B \mid C)] + P^* (B \mid A) \right) \qquad (4)$$

Related local patterns of inference for interval-valued conditional probabilities have been independently developed in the contexts of deductive databases ([Güntzer91], [Thöne91a]) and of terminological languages [Heinsohn91] respectively.

Recently, Thöne, Güntzer and Kießling [Thöne91a] have pointed out that the above upper bound can be improved when only lower and upper bounds on the probabilities are available in the syllogism. This is basically due to the fact that the third and fourth terms are linearly increasing with respect to P(B|A) while the second term is linearly decreasing in P(B|A) if P*(C|B < P*(A|B). These authors show that the upper bound is optimal provided that we add the following fifth term in the above minimum of four terms:

$$\frac{P^* (C \mid B)}{P^* (C \mid B) + P_* (B \mid C) \cdot (P_* (A \mid B) - P^* (C \mid B))}$$

This fifth term is simply obtained by computing the value of P(B | A) that makes the second and third term equal. This fifth term does improve the upper bound if and only if P*(A | B) > P*(C | B)

$$P_* (B \mid A) \leq \frac{P_* (B \mid C) \cdot P_* (A \mid B)}{P_* (B \mid C) \cdot P_* (A \mid B) + P^* (C \mid B) \cdot (1 - P_* (B \mid C))} \leq P^* (B \mid A)$$

Let us point out that it is easy to generalize these formulas to quantifiers whose values are fuzzily known, i.e. [p*, p*] is replaced by a fuzzy interval ([Dubois88]), but it is not the purpose of this paper.

Moreover, considering the network of Figure 3, it can be checked that Pattern I is associative, i.e. we obtain the same bounds if the pattern is applied to nodes A, B and C first ("eliminating" B) and then to nodes A, C and D, as shown in part (α) of Fig. 3, or if we proceed as indicated in part (β) of this figure, i.e. "eliminating" C by considering nodes B, C and D first.

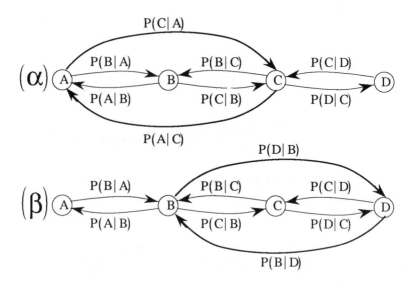

Figure 3   Associativity.

See Annex 1, where we study lower bounds of P(D / A) in both (α) and (β). The case of the upper bound can be checked similarly but is more tedious.

In fact, the deep reason for associativity is that the repeated use of Pattern I in a chain <A B C D> like the one pictured in Figure 3 still provides optimal bounds for P(D | A) and P(A | D). This is due to a property of the linear programming problem underlying the pattern, where it is possible to eliminate a node by introducing new variables (i.e., using the notations of section 3, stating $x_i, k, l = x_i, 0, k, l + x_i, 1, k, l$ for eliminating B for instance). In other words, the values of P(C | D) and P(D | C) do not affect the optimal bounds of P(C | A) and P(A | C).

Clearly, this property of Pattern I is very nice and easily generalises to a network with any number of nodes. Thus on a "linear chain" (like networks in Figure 3) beginning with node A_1 and ending with node A_n, we can apply Pattern I iteratively, from left to right, in order to evaluate P(A_n | A_1) for instance, without resorting to linear programming.

6   CONJUNCTION OF EVENTS

In this section we are interested in estimating the proportion of A's and B's which are C's, and more generally P(C | A $\cap$ B), and the proportion of C's which are A's and B's, and more generally P(A $\cap$ B | C). To do so, we are going to present two patterns in order to evaluate optimal lower and upper bounds for P(C I A ∩ B) and P(A ∩ B I C).

6.1   Pattern II

Here we want to answer a query concerning P(C I A ∩ B) as pictured in Figure 4:

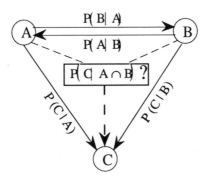

Figure 4   Pattern II.

To evaluate the lower bound, we use the following trivial inequalities:

$$P(A \cap B \cap C) \geq 0$$
$$P(A \cap B \cap C) \geq P(A \cap B) + P(A \cap C) - P(A)$$
$$P(A \cap B \cap C) \geq P(A \cap B) + P(B \cap C) - P(B)$$

and we derive the following lower bound, which can be proved to be optimal ([Dubois90]):

$$P_*(C \mid A \cap B) = \max \left(0,\, 1 - \frac{1 - P(C \mid A)}{P(B \mid A)},\, 1 - \frac{1 - P(C \mid B)}{P(A \mid B)} \right) \qquad (5)$$

(5) is extended to imprecisely-known conditional probabilities as follows:

$$P_*(C \mid A \cap B) = \max \left(0,\, 1 - \frac{1 - P_*(C \mid A)}{P_*(B \mid A)},\, 1 - \frac{1 - P_*(C \mid B)}{P_*(A \mid B)} \right) \qquad (6)$$

For the upper bound, using the three following inequalities,

$$P(A \cap B \cap C) \le P(A \cap B);$$
$$P(A \cap B \cap C) \le P(A \cap C);$$
$$P(A \cap B \cap C) \le P(B \cap C);$$

we derive the optimal upper bound ([Dubois90]):

$$P^*(C \mid A \cap B) = \min\left(1, \frac{P(C \mid A)}{P(B \mid A)}, \frac{P(C \mid B)}{P(A \mid B)}\right) \tag{7}$$

(7) is extended to imprecisely-known conditional probabilities as follows:

$$P^*(C \mid A \cap B) = \min\left(1, \frac{P^*(C \mid A)}{P_*(B \mid A)}, \frac{P^*(C \mid B)}{P_*(A \mid B)}\right) \tag{8}$$

6.2   Pattern III

We want now to evaluate the proportion of the C's which are A's and B's. In the framework of conditional probabilities, the problem is equivalent to find $P(A \cap B \mid C)$, in terms of $P(A \mid C)$ and $P(B \mid C)$. So we study the following pattern pictured in Figure 5:

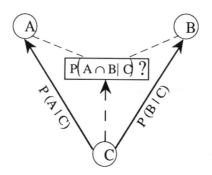

Figure 5   Pattern III.

It is well known that:

$$\max(0, P(A \mid C) + P(B \mid C) - 1) \le P(A \cap B \mid C) \le \min((P(A \mid C), P(B \mid C))$$

so:

$$P_*(A \cap B \mid C) = \max(0, P(A \mid C) + P(B \mid C) - 1) \tag{9}$$

$$P^*(A \cap B \mid C) = \min(P(A \mid C), P(B \mid C) \tag{10}$$

and, when generalising to intervals:

$$P_*(A \cap B \mid C) = \max(0, P_*(A \mid C) + P_*(B \mid C) - 1) \tag{11}$$

$$P^*(A \cap B \mid C) = \min(P^*(A \mid C), P^*(B \mid C)) \tag{12}$$

These bounds are known to be optimal. In Pattern III P(A | B) and P(B | A) do not appear since it is proved in [Dubois90] that their knowledge does lead to improve the bounds (11) and (12).

7   DISJUNCTION OF EVENTS

Now, we want to evaluate the proportion of the A's or B's which are C's (and more generally P(C | A ∪ B)), and the proportion of the C's which are A's or B's (and more generally P(A ∪ B | C)). To do so, we study two patterns which are dual of the ones presented for the conjunction, in order to determine lower and upper bounds for P(C | A ∪ B) and P(A ∪ B | C).

7.1   Pattern IV

We consider the following pattern:

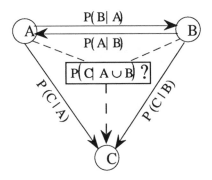

Figure 6 Pattern IV.

Contrary to Pattern II, here we are able to work directly at the conditional probabilities level, and we find (see proof in Annex 2):

$$P(C \mid A \cup B) = \frac{\dfrac{P(C \mid A)}{P(B \mid A)} + \dfrac{P(C \mid B)}{P(A \mid B)} - P(C \mid A \cap B)}{\dfrac{1}{P(B \mid A)} + \dfrac{1}{P(A \mid B)} - 1} \tag{13}$$

To get upper and lower bounds from (13), it is enough to replace $P(C \mid A \cap B)$ by its lower and upper bounds, respectively (see equations (5) and (7)):

- upper bound: with (5) we get:

$$P^*(C \mid A \cup B) = \min \left(1, \frac{\dfrac{P(C \mid A)}{P(B \mid A)} + \dfrac{P(C \mid B)}{P(A \mid B)}}{\dfrac{1}{P(B \mid A)} + \dfrac{1}{P(A \mid B)} - 1} \right. ,$$

$$\frac{\dfrac{P(C \mid A)}{P(B \mid A)} + \dfrac{1 - P(A \mid B)}{P(A \mid B)}}{\dfrac{1}{P(B \mid A)} + \dfrac{1}{P(A \mid B)} - 1} , \tag{14}$$

$$\left. \frac{\dfrac{1 - P(B \mid A)}{P(B \mid A)} + \dfrac{P(C \mid B)}{P(A \mid B)}}{\dfrac{1}{P(B \mid A)} + \dfrac{1}{P(A \mid B)} - 1} \right)$$

- lower bound: with (7) we get:

$$P_*(C \mid A \cup B) = \frac{\max\left(\dfrac{P(C \mid A)}{P(B \mid A)} + \dfrac{P(C \mid B)}{P(A \mid B)} - 1, \dfrac{P(C \mid A)}{P(B \mid A)}, \dfrac{P(C \mid B)}{P(A \mid B)} \right)}{\dfrac{1}{P(B \mid A)} + \dfrac{1}{P(A \mid B)} - 1} \tag{15}$$

The behaviour of these expressions with respect to $P(A \mid B)$ and $P(B \mid A)$ is not simple.

7.2   Pattern V

Here, we want to answer the query "what proportion of C's are A's or B's?", i.e. we want to evaluate $P(A \cup B \mid C) \in [(P_*(A \cup B \mid C), P^*(A \cup B \mid C))$. This corresponds to Pattern V pictured in Figure 7.

It is well known that:

$$\max(P(A \mid C), P(B \mid C)) \le P(A \cup B \mid C) \le \min(1, P(A \mid C) + P(B \mid C)) \quad (16)$$

so we have, when generalising (16) to imprecisely-known conditional probabilities, for the lower bound:

$$P_*(A \cup B \mid C) = \max(P_*(A \mid C), P_*(B \mid C)) \quad (17)$$

and, for the upper bound:

$$P^*(A \cup B \mid C) = \max(1, P^*(A|C) + P^*(B|C)) \quad (18)$$

These bounds are optimal and in Pattern V, $P(A \mid B)$ and $P(B \mid A)$ do not appear since it is proved in [Dubois90] that their knowledge does lead to improve the bounds (17) and (18).

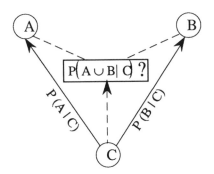

Figure 7   Pattern V.

8   DEALING WITH NEGATION

It is interesting to be able to answer queries involving negation. Namely we want to estimate the proportion of A's which are not B's (more generally $P(\neg B \mid A)$), and the proportion of not B's which are A's (more generally $P(A \mid \neg B)$) from information about $P(A \mid B)$ and $P(B \mid A)$. The situation is sketched in Figure 8.

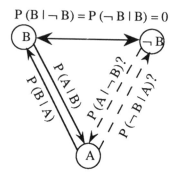

Figure 8   Pattern I with negation.

Since $P(\neg B \mid A) = 1 - P(B \mid A)$, we obviously have: $P_*(\neg B \mid A) = 1 - P^*(B \mid A)$, and, $P^*(\neg B \mid A) = 1 - P_*(B \mid A)$.

Applying to Bayes' theorem two times:

$$\frac{P(A \mid B)}{P(B \mid A)} = \frac{P(A)}{P(B)} \quad \text{and} \quad \frac{P(\neg B \mid A)}{P(A \mid \neg B)} = \frac{P(\neg B)}{P(A)}$$

it becomes,

$$\frac{P(A \mid B)}{P(B \mid A)} \frac{P(\neg B \mid A)}{P(A \mid \neg B)} = \frac{P(\neg B)}{P(B)}$$

and we finally obtain the following expression for $P(A \mid \neg B)$,

$$P(A \mid \neg B) = \frac{P(A \mid B)}{P(B \mid A)} (1 - P(B \mid A)) \frac{P(B)}{P(\neg B)} \qquad (19)$$

From the above formula it is clear that $P(A \mid \neg B)$ can take any value between 0 and 1, according to the value of $P(B)$ which is unknown a priori. In order to get more precise results, we have to estimate the quantity $\frac{P(B)}{P(\neg B)}$. In order to do it, we may use a closed world assumption (CWA). In our framework, the closed world assumption can be stated as follows: If sets A, B, and C_i, $i \in$]n] appear in the network, then let us assume that the universe is reduced to $A \cup B \cup \bigcup_{i \in [n]} C_i$. In other words, we assume that the set $\neg A \cap \neg B \cap \bigcap_{i \in [n]} \neg C_i$ is empty, or at least that $P(\neg A \cap \neg B \cap \bigcap_{i \in [n]} \neg C_i) = 0$.

In the trivial case where we consider the classes A and B only, it leads to $P(\neg A \cap \neg B) = 0$, and then:

$$P(A \mid \neg B) = \frac{P(A \cap \neg B)}{P(\neg B)} = \frac{P(A \cap \neg B) + P(\neg A \cap \neg B)}{P(\neg B)} = 1 = P(A \mid A \cap \neg B)$$

If we "open" the world by considering C also, then we assume $P(\neg A \cap \neg B \cap \neg C) = 0$.

Since $\neg B = [\neg B \cap (A \cup C)] \cup [\neg B \cap \neg (A \cup C)] = \neg B \cap (A \cup C) \cup (\neg A \cap \neg B \cap \neg C)$. Then $P(\neg B) = P(\neg B \cap (A \cup C))$. Thus we change the question "what is the value of $P(A \mid \neg B)$?" into "what is the value of $P(A \mid \neg B \cap (A \cup C))$?". A systematic way of dealing with these questions requires a proper handling of Boolean expressions in conditional probability, and this is beyond the scope of this paper.

9   GLOBAL REASONING WITH LOCAL PATTERNS

In the previous sections, we have presented local patterns, and now the problem is to use these patterns in order to reason with the whole network. So, the aim of this section is to build a reasoning strategy in order to be able to answer any simple query (i.e. a query of the form "what is the proportion of A's and B's which are C's?", where A, B and C are atoms in the language).

We will first use a saturation strategy in order to extract as much information as we can from the network, namely, try to get probability intervals as tight as possible for all conditional probabilities $P(A \mid B)$. The result is called the saturated network.

9.1   Saturation Procedure:

We are going to use two tools: Pattern I (corresponding to the basic syllogism) presented in section 5, in order to add links to the network, and the generalised Bayes' theorem presented in section 4.

Step 1: recursively apply Pattern I, to generate the missing arcs. This step is performed until the probability intervals can no longer be improved.

Step 2: recursively apply the generalised Bayes' theorem to improve the arcs generated by Step 1. This is performed until it is no longer possible to improve bounds.

Then, the general algorithm is:

a. perform Step 1

b. perform Step 2

c. if the probability intervals have been improved go to (a), otherwise stop.

Note that the two steps are very complementary. Indeed, Step 1 uses an optimal rule but a local one, while Step 2 uses a suboptimal method but considers more than 3-uples of nodes.

Another important problem encountered in the inference system is the consistency of the knowledge base.

9.2   Tools for Checking Consistency

Using the global method presented in section 3, if one of the two linear programs we have to solve (or both) has no solution (i.e. no starting feasible base), we can say that there is an inconsistency in the constraints of the linear programs, i.e. an inconsistency in the knowledge base.

Then we will use the global method (with a simple query, i.e. of the form "what is the value of $P(B \mid A)$?") to test the consistency of the knowledge base. Let us note that solving only one linear program is enough to find out an inconsistency (if any) among the constraints expressing the knowledge base. If there is some inconsistency, exhibiting the Simplex array, we will be able to determine where the inconsistency is, i.e. which arcs are inconsistent.

9.3   A Sketch of the General System

So, our system is of the following general form:

a. consistency checking if an inconsistency is detected, exit;

b. saturation of the network;

c. answering user's queries. The considered queries are presently of the form $P(A \mid B)$?, $P(A \cup B \mid C)$?, $P(A \cap B \mid C)$?, $P(C \mid A \cap B)$?, ...

Of course, steps (a) and (b) may take a long time to compute, but they are only performed once and for all at the beginning of the session, in order to ensure that the user works with a consistent knowledge base, and to make all the information explicit.

10 QUERIES INVOLVING CONJUNCTIONS AND DISJUNCTIONS

The patterns involving conjunctions solved above are not general enough to be very useful in practice. Their merits are but tutorial. Their extensión to disjunctions and conjunctions of more than two terms, especially looks intractable in an analytic form. Even the case when only three symbols A, B and C are involved, and where bounds on the six conditional probability values involving these symbols are known will lead to unwieldy expressions because the six values are related via the generalised Bayes' theorem.

A more realistic approach to the problem of handling disjunctions and conjunctions is to introduce new nodes in the network, that account for the concerned conjunctions and disjunctions, and apply the iterative algorithm (or the linear programming one) to answer the query. As an example, let us consider the query "what is the probability of C given A and B", where the background network includes nodes A, B, C only (see Figure 9).

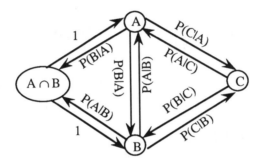

Figure 9 Introducing a new node "A ∩ B".

To deal with this problem we create a node named A ∩ B. A complete description of the conjunction in terms of conditional probabilities leads to force $P_*(A \mid A \cap B) = 1$, $P_*(B \mid A \cap B) = 1$, $P(A \cap B \mid B) = P(A \mid B)$ and $P(A \cap B \mid A) = P(B \mid A)$, and to add these arcs to the network (see Figure 9). Then the calculation of $P(C \mid A \cap B)$ comes down to the repeated use of the syllogism pattern and the generalised Bayes' rule in this network. In order to catch a feeling of what kinds of results can be produced by this method, let us deal with the case when the six values $P(A \mid C)$, $P(C \mid A)$, $P(B \mid C)$, $P(C \mid B)$, $P(A \mid B)$, $P(B \mid A)$ are precisely known in Figure 9. Of course they obey the generalized Bayes theorem, so that only five of them need to be known. The calculation of bounds for $P(C \mid A \cap B)$ can be performed by applying twice the syllogism rule, cancelling A between A ∩ B and C, and cancelling B between A ∩ B and C.

Applying (1) and (3) with the following substitution: A becomes A ∩ B, B becomes A, we get

$$\max\left(0,\ 1-\frac{1-P(C\mid A)}{P(B\mid A)}\right)\le P(C\mid A\cap B)\le \min\left(1,\frac{P(C\mid A)}{P(B\mid A)}\right)$$

Similarly, exchanging A and B in the above inequalities, we get:

$$\max\left(0,\ 1-\frac{1-P(C\mid A)}{P(B\mid A)}\right)\le P(C\mid A\cap B)\le \min\left(1,\frac{P(C\mid B)}{P(A\mid B)}\right)$$

Joining these results together, we get the equations (5) and (7) already computed, we obtain

$$\max\left(0,\ 1-\frac{1-P(C\mid A)}{P(B\mid A)},\ 1-\frac{1-P(C\mid B)}{P(A\mid B)}\right)\le P(C\mid A\cap B)$$

$$P(C\mid A\cap B)\le \min\left(1,\frac{P(C\mid A)}{P(B\mid A)},\frac{P(C\mid B)}{P(A\mid B)}\right)$$

It can be checked that this is exactly what has been obtained in section 6, i.e. when we have no knowledge about P(B | C) and P(A | C). To improve these bounds requires the use of the generalised Bayes' theorem. As shown in [Dubois90], only the lower bound of P(C | A ∩ B) can be improved knowing P(B | C) and P(A | C). However this indicates that the above inequalities do not yield an optimal lower bound to P(C | A ∩ B). Proceeding similarly for P(A ∩ B | C), the syllogism rule leads to the following bounds.

$$\max\left[0,\ P(A\mid C)\left(1+\frac{P(B\mid A)-1}{P(C\mid A)}\right),\ P(B\mid C)\left(1+\frac{P(A\mid B)-1}{P(C\mid B)}\right)\right]$$

$$\le P(A\cap B\mid C)\le$$

$$\min\left(P(A\mid C),\ P(B\mid C),\ \frac{P(A\mid C)\,P(B\mid A)}{P(C\mid A)},\ \frac{P(B\mid C)\,P(A\mid B)}{P(C\mid B)}\right)$$

Note that in the above expression, the two last terms in the 'min' are equal due to Bayes' theorem. Using results in [Dubois90], it can be checked that the upper bound is optimal while the lower bound is sound but not optimal. Indeed we do not recover the obvious bound

$$P(A \cap B \mid C) \geq \max(0, P(A \mid C) + P(B \mid C) - 1)$$

More specifically, given only $P(A \mid C) = 1$ and $P(B \mid C) = 1$, the repeated use of the syllogism rule and the generalised Bayes' rule are not capable of producing $P(A \cap B \mid C) = 1$ (a result produced by the above bound). Indeed, if we add the node AB to represent $A \cap B$, we have to saturate the following network (Figure 10):

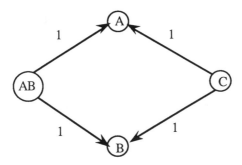

Figure 10

All that this network tells us is that $AB \subseteq A \cap B$ and $C \subseteq A \cap B$, but clearly, $AB \cap C$ can be anything. Clearly, even assuming that $P(A \mid B) \neq 1$ and $P(B \mid A) \neq 1$ are known and letting $P(AB \mid A) = P(B \mid A)$, $P(AB \mid B) = P(A \mid B)$ cannot improve the lower bound of $P(AB \mid C)$ using the syllogism rule, nor the generalised Bayes' rule. This point indicates that the basic lower bounds obtained in section 6, for the conjunction will be useful to keep, in order to improve the performance of the iterative procedure.

Another point to notice is that the constraint $P(AB \mid A) = P(B \mid A)$ is different from letting $P^*(AB \mid A) = P^*(B \mid A)$, $P_*(AB \mid A) = P_*(B \mid A)$, when only bounds on $P(B \mid A)$ are known; indeed, the equality of the bounds can go along with the inequality $P(AB \mid A) \neq P(B \mid A)$.

Let us consider the query about $P(C \mid A \cup B)$. To deal with this case, we create a node named $A \cup B$, and arcs joining this node to the network, so as to describe the disjunction in terms of conditional probabilities, namely

P(A ∪ B | A) = 1 and P(A ∪ B | B) = 1. The calculation of P(A | A ∪ B) and P(B | A ∪ B) is slightly less straightforward, namely

$$P(A \mid A \cup B) = \frac{P(A)}{P(A \cup B)} = \frac{P(A)}{P(A) + P(B) - P(A \cap B)} = \frac{1}{1 + \dfrac{P(B)}{P(A)} - P(B \mid A)}$$

$$= \frac{P(A \mid B)}{P(A \mid B) + P(B \mid A) - P(A \mid B) \cdot P(B \mid A)} \ ,$$

since $\dfrac{P(B)}{P(A)} = \dfrac{P(B \mid A)}{P(A \mid B)}$

The complete study of this case is left to the reader. Difficulties similar to the ones encountered with conjunctions will be observed.

11   AN EXAMPLE

In this section, our purpose is to point out the results given by both Pattern I and generalised Bayes' theorem.

The algorithm we use is:

Step 1: apply Pattern I until it is no longer possible to generate new arcs nor to improve bounds;

Step 2: apply generalised Bayes' theorem;

Step 3: if the network is not saturated, goto Step 1.

This algorithm is written in "C" on a Sun 3/50 workstation without arithmetical co-processor and the algorithm used to compute the longest paths is Floyd's (see [Gondran85]).

The example we use is already considered in [Dubois90], and is pictured in Figure 11.

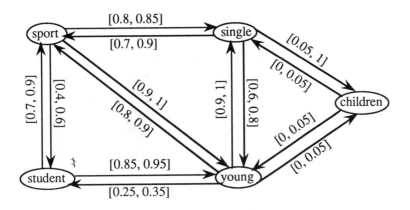

Figure 11   Example extracted from [Dubois90].

In the following, we will use the incidence matrix notation to let the saturated network be more readable. Thus, for the network of Figure 11, the incidence matrix is[1]:

input data	student	sport	single	young	children
student	[1.000, 1.000]	[0.700, 0.900]	[0.000, 1.000]	[0.850, 0.950]	[0.000, 1.000]
sport	[0.400, 0.600]	[1.000, 1.000]	[0.800, 0.850]	[0.900, 1.000]	[0.000, 1.000]
single	[0.000, 1.000]	[0.700, 0.900]	[1.000, 1.000]	[0.600, 0.800]	[0.050, 0.100]
young	[0.250, 0.350]	[0.800, 0.900]	[0.900, 1.000]	[1.000, 1.000]	[0.000, 0.050]
children	[0.000, 1.000]	[0.000, 1.000]	[0.000, 0.050]	[0.000, 0.050]	[1.000, 1.000]

Now we go through the algorithm, using the following notations:

PatternI(A, C) via B = [lower bound, upper bound] means that Pattern I generates an arc between A and C, or improves the bounds of the arc <A;C>, using B as intermediary node (see Figure 2 in section 5). Similarly, GenBayes(A, B) = [lower bound, upper bound] means that

---

1   A valuation [0,1] for an element (i,j) of the matrix signifies that there is no arc between i and j in the input network; e.g (student, single) = [0,1].

the generalised Bayes' theorem improves the bounds of the arc <A; B>.
In both cases, the improved bounds are <u>underlined</u>.

Step 1:   apply Pattern I until it is no longer possible to generate new arcs nor
to improve bounds

**** IMPROVEMENTS GIVEN BY PATTERN I : PASS 1

PatternI(student, single) via sport	= [<u>0.350000</u> , 1.000000]
PatternI(student, single) via young	= [<u>0.510000</u> , 1.000000]
PatternI(student, children) via young	= [0.000000 , <u>0.320000</u>]
PatternI(sport, student) via young	= [0.400000 , <u>0.493750</u>]
PatternI(sport, young) via single	= [0.900000 , <u>0.957937</u>]
PatternI(sport, children) via student	= [0.000000 , <u>0.782857</u>]
PatternI(sport, children) via single	= [0.000000 , <u>0.314286</u>]
PatternI(sport, children) via young	= [0.000000 , <u>0.156250</u>]
PatternI(single, student) via sport	= [<u>0.175000</u> , <u>0.732031</u>]
PatternI(single, student) via young	= [0.175000 , <u>0.366013</u>]
PatternI(single, sport) via young	= [0.700000 , <u>0.888889</u>]
PatternI(single, young) via sport	= [<u>0.612500</u> , 0.800000]
PatternI(young, student) via sport	= [<u>0.266667</u> , 0.350000]
PatternI(young, single) via sport	= [0.900000 , <u>0.955556</u>]
PatternI(children, student) via single	= [0.000000 , <u>0.401660</u>]
PatternI(children, sport) via single	= [0.000000 , <u>0.272222</u>]

**** IMPROVEMENTS GIVEN BY PATTERN I : PASS 2

PatternI(student, single) via young	= [<u>0.531250</u> , 1.000000]
PatternI(student, children) via young	= [0.000000 , <u>0.309375</u>]
PatternI(sport, student) via young	= [0.400000 , <u>0.493056</u>]
PatternI(children, student) via single	= [0.000000 , <u>0.372953</u>]

*** IMPROVEMENTS GIVEN BY PATTERN I : PASS 3 : *STABILITY*

Then, because it is no longer possible to generate arcs nor to improve bounds
using Pattern I, the system goes through Step 2:

Step 2:   apply generalised Bayes' theorem (this is performed in one step using
a longest path algorithm)

**** IMPROVEMENTS GIVEN BY GENERALIZED BAYES' THEOREM:

GenBayes(student, sport)	= [<u>0.900000</u> , 0.900000]
GenBayes(student, young)	= [0.850000 , <u>0.850000</u>]
GenBayes(sport, student)	= [0.400000 , <u>0.400000</u>]

GenBayes(sport, single)   = [0.850000 , 0.850000]
GenBayes(single, student)   = [0.194444 , 0.366013]
GenBayes(single, sport)   = [0.700000 , 0.700000]
GenBayes(single, young)   = [0.800000 , 0.800000]
GenBayes(young, student)   = [0.350000 , 0.350000]
GenBayes(young, sport)   = [0.833823 , 0.887500]
GenBayes(young, single)   = [0.900000 , 0.900000]
GenBayes(children, student)   = [0.000000 , 0.113235]
GenBayes(children, sport)   = [0.000000 , 0.128677]
GenBayes(children, young)   = [0.000000 , 0.044444]

Then, because some improvements have been made, the system goes back to Step 1, applying Pattern I:

**** IMPROVEMENTS GIVEN BY PATTERN I : PASS 1
PatternI(student, single) via sport   = [0.562500 , 1.000000]
PatternI(student, single) via young   = [0.607143 , 1.000000]
PatternI(student, children) via young   = [0.000000 , 0.271429]
PatternI(sport, children) via young   = [0.000000 , 0.153968]
PatternI(single, student) via sport   = [0.205882 , 0.366013]
PatternI(single, student) via young   = [0.222222 , 0.366013]

*** IMPROVEMENTS GIVEN BY PATTERN I: PASS 2: *STABILITY*
And, because the network is not saturated yet, the system performs Step 2:

*** IMPROVEMENTS GIVEN BY GENERALISED BAYES' THEOREM:
GenBayes(student, young)   = [0.850000 , 0.850000]
GenBayes(children, student)   = [0.000000 , 0.099346]
GenBayes(children, sport)   = [0.000000 , 0.126797]

Going through the algorithm, the system performs Step 1, giving:

*** IMPROVEMENTS GIVEN BY PATTERN I: PASS 1:
SATURATION

And, performing step 2:

*** IMPROVEMENTS GIVEN BY GENERALIZED BAYES' THEOREM:
SATURATION

So, we get the "saturated" network, with the following incidence matrix (the improved bounds are given in **bold**):

saturated network	student	sport	single	young	children
student	[1.000,1.000]	[**0.900**,0.900]	[**0.607**,1.000]	[0.850,**0.850**]	[0.000,**0.271**]
sport	[0.400,**0.400**]	[1.000,1.000]	[**0.850**,0.850]	[0.900,**0.958**]	[0.000,**0.154**]
single	[**0.222,0.366**]	[**0.700,0.700**]	[1.000,1.000]	[**0.800**,0.800]	[0.050,0.100]
young	[**0.350**,0.350]	[**0.834,0.888**]	[0.900,**0.900**]	[1.000,1.000]	[0.000,0.050]
children	[0.000,**0.099**]	[0.000,**0.127**]	[0.000,**0.050**]	[0.000,**0.044**]	[1.000,1.000]

The computation of the complete "saturated" matrix was made in 10 seconds (CPU and I/O time).

The optimal solution computed by the global method presented in section 3 and in [Amarger90] is (in an incidence matrix form):

optimal solution	student	sport	single	young	children
student	[1.000,1.000]	[0.900,0.900]	[0.607,1.000]	[0.850,0.850]	[0.000,0.271]
sport	[0.400,0.400]	[1.000,1.000]	[0.850,0.850]	[0.900,0.958]	[0.000,0.154]
single	[0.222,0.366]	[0.700,0.700]	[1.000,1.000]	[0.800,0.800]	[0.050,0.100]
young	[0.350,0.350]	[0.834,0.888]	[0.900,0.900]	[1.000,1.000]	[0.000,0.050]
children	[0.000,0.099]	[0.000,0.127]	[0.000,0.050]	[0.000,0.044]	[1.000,1.000]

This matrix is exactly the same as the one computed by the "local method" based on Pattern I and generalised Bayes' theorem.

Let us note that the "global method" is written in "C", on a Sun 3/50 workstation, without arithmetical co-processor; and the computation of each element of the "optimal" matrix is made in 12 seconds (CPU and I/O time).

So, combining a locally optimal method (Pattern I) with a global but sub-optimal method (generalised Bayes' theorem), we get results as good as the ones given by a globally optimal method (Simplex-based method of section 3), but with a much smaller computation time, in our example.

12   CONCLUSION

The approach proposed in this paper to handle conditional probabilities in knowledge networks presupposes assumptions that contrast with the ones underlying Bayesian networks. In Bayesian networks, a single joint probability distribution is reconstructed from the acyclic network using conditional independence assumptions, and given some a priori probabilities on the roots of the acyclic network. Here, nothing is assumed about a priori (unconditional) probabilities, no independence assumption is taken for granted, and, the more cycles there are, the more informative the network is.

Results obtained so far indicate that the two inference rules that we use in turn, namely the syllogism rule (Pattern I) and the generalised Bayes' theorem, are powerful and can compete with a brute force linear programming approach, as regards the quality of the obtained probability bounds. Our inference technique seems to be more efficient than linear programming since each run of each step of the inference procedure is polynomial in the number of nodes in the network. However, more investigation is needed on complexity aspects, and to better grasp the distance to optimality of the inference procedure.

It has been indicated how to deal with conditional probabilities involving conjunctions, disjunctions and negation of terms. However, the obtained optimal bounds are rather heavy mathematical expressions for conjunctions and disjunctions, and it seems difficult to extrapolate them to more than two terms. Moreover probabilities of the form $P(A \mid \neg B)$ are generally very badly known, except if closed world assumptions are made. In the future, we plan to solve the problem of conjunction, disjunction and negation by introducing auxiliary nodes in the original network. For instance, a query about $P(C \mid A \cup B)$ can be addressed by introducing a special node called "$A \cup B$" which is related to the remainder of the network by arcs $<A, A \cup B>$ with $P(A \cup B \mid A) = 1$ and $<B, A \cup B>$ with $P(A \cup B \mid B) = 1$. This solution will be investigated in the future, since it easily generalises to the combination of more than two primitive terms.

In the long run, we plan to develop a computerised tool (parts of which are already implemented) that can handle a knowledge base in the form of a pair (W, Δ) where W is a set of facts and Δ a set of conditional probabilities. A query Q can then be solved by computing $P(Q \mid W)$ where W is the conjunction of available facts, and $P(Q \mid W)$ is obtained under the form of bounds derived from the saturated network built with Δ.

Among topics of interest for future research, a more detailed comparison with the Bayesian approach would be quite interesting, of course. It would allow the loss of information due to the absence of a priori probabilities to be quantified. An important problem is how to allow for independence assumptions in our approach. Clearly it generates non-linear constraints in the optimisation problem associated to a query. But it seems that the inference procedure can cope with these assumptions in a nicer way (see e.g. [Thöne91]).

Another topic is the extension of our method to fuzzy quantifiers, already considered in [Dubois88] for the syllogism rule.

Lastly, it would be fruitful to study the analogy between our kind of probabilistic reasoning and non-monotonic logics.

ACKNOWLEDGEMENT

This work is partially supported by the DRUMS project (Defeasible Reasoning and Uncertainty Management Systems), funded by the Commission of the European Communities under the ESPRIT Basic Research Action number 3085.

REFERENCES

Amarger, S., Epenoy, R. and Grihon, S. (1990) Reasoning with conditional probabilities. A linear programming based method. In Proceedings of the DRUMS RP2 Workshop, Basic Research Esprit Project DRUMS, IRIT – Toulouse (France), pp. 154-167, April.

Amarger, S., Dubois, D. and Prade, H (1991) Constraint propagation with imprecise conditional probabilities. Proc. 7th Conf. on Uncertainty in Artificial Intelligence, UCLA, Los Angeles, July 13–18, Morgan and Kaufmann, Palo Alto, Ca. 26–34.

Charnes, A. and Cooper, W.W. (1962) Programming with linear fractional functions. Naval Res. Logist. Quart. 9, pp. 181–186.

Dubois, D. and Prade, H. (1988) On fuzzy syllogisms. Computational Intelligence 4, pp. 171–179.

Dubois, D., Prade, H. and Toucas, J.-M. (1990) Inference with imprecise numerical quantifiers. In Intelligent Systems: State of the Art and Future Directions. Ellis Horwood Ltd., Z. Ras and M. Zemankova (Eds).

Gondran, M. and Minoux, M. (1985) Graphes et algorithmes, EYROLLES, Paris.

Güntzer, U., Kießling, W. and Thöne, H (1991) New directions for uncertainty reasoning in deductive databases. Proc. ACM SIGMOD Inter. Conf. on Management of Data, Denver, 178–187.

Heinsohn, J. (1991) A hybrid approach for modelling uncertainty in terminological logics. In: Symbolic and Quantitative Approaches to Uncertainty. Proc. of Europ. Conf. ECSQAU, Marseille, October, R. Kruse and P. Siegel (Eds), Lecture Notes in Computer Science, Vol. 548, Springer Verlag, Berlin, 198–205. Complete version: Research Report no. RR–91–24, Deutsches Forschungszentrum für Künstliche Intelligenz GmbH, Saarbrücken, Germany.

Lauritzen, S.L. and Spiegelhalter, D.J. (1988) Local computation with probabilities on graphical structures and their application to expert systems. Journal of the Royal Statistical Society, B 50, 2, pp. 157–224.

Besnard, P., Cordier, M.-O., Dubois, D., Fariñas del Cerro, L., Froidevaux, C., Moinard, Y., Prade, H., Schwind, C. and Siegel, P. (1990) Reasoning Under Incomplete Information in Artificial Intelligence: a comparison of formalisms using a single example, Wiley, New York.

Paass, G. (1988) Probabilistic Logic. In Non-Standard Logics for Automated Reasoning. Academic Press, Didier Dubois Philippe Smets, Abe Mamdani and Henri Prade (Eds.), Ch. 8, pp. 213–251.

Pearl, J. (1988) Probabilistic Reasoning in Intelligent Systems: networks of plausible inference, Morgan Kaufmann Publishers.

Schaible, S. and Ibaraki, T. (1983) Fractional programming. European Journal of Operation Research, 12, pp. 325–338.

Thöne, H., Güntzer, U. and Kießling, W. (1991a) Probabilistic reasoning with facts and rules in deductive databases. In: Symbolic and Quantitative Approaches to Uncertainty. Proc. of the Europ. Conf. ECSQAU, Marseille, October, R. Kruse and P. Siegel (Eds), Lecture Notes in Computer Science, Vol. 548, Springer Cerlag, Berlin, 333–337.

Thöne, H., Güntzer, U. and Kießling, W. (1991b) Towards precision of probabilistic bounds propagation. Report Wilhelm-Schickard-Institut, Universität Tübingen, Germany.

van der Gaag, L.C. (1990a) Probability-Based Models for Plausible Reasoning, PhD thesis, University of Amsterdam.

van der Gaag, L.C. (1990b) Computing probability intervals under independecy constraints, in Proceedings of the Sixth Conference on Uncertainty in Artificial Intelligence, 27-29 July, Cambridge, Mass., pp. 491–495.

Zadeh, L.A. (1985) Syllogistic reasoning in fuzzy logic and its application to usuality and reasoning with dispositions. IEEE Trans. on Systems, Man and Cybernetics, 15, 6, pp. 745–763.

ANNEX 1

Proof of the associativity of Pattern I: case of the lower bound

In network (α): we apply Pattern I to compute $P_*(C \mid A)$ and $P_*(A \mid C)$, so, applying Pattern I a second time, we evaluate a first value for $P_*(D \mid A)$, which gives:

$$P_{\alpha*} (D \mid A) =$$

$$\frac{P_*(B \mid A)}{P_*(A \mid B)} \max \left[0, P_*(A \mid B) + \frac{P_*(C \mid B)}{P_*(B \mid C)} \max[0, P_*(B \mid C) + P_*(D \mid C) - 1] - 1 \right]$$

While in network (β): we apply Pattern I to compute $P_*(B \mid D)$ and $P_*(D \mid B)$, so, applying Pattern I a second time, we evaluate a new value for $P_*(D \mid A)$, which gives:

$$P_{\beta*} (D \mid A) =$$

$$\frac{P_*(C \mid A)}{P_*(A \mid C)} \max \left[0, P_*(D \mid C) + \frac{P_*(B \mid C)}{P_*(C \mid B)} \max[0, P_*(C \mid B) + P_*(A \mid B) - 1] - 1 \right]$$

So, we have to prove that $P_{\alpha*}(DjA) = P_{\beta*}(D \mid A)$:

Developing, we get:

$$P_{\alpha*} (D \mid A) =$$

$$\frac{P_*(C \mid A)}{P_*(A \mid C)} \max \left[0, P_*(D \mid C) + P_*(B \mid C) + \frac{P_*(B \mid C)P_*(A \mid B)}{P_*(C \mid B)} - \frac{P_*(B \mid C)}{P_*(C \mid B)} - 1 \right]$$

$$P_{\beta*} (D \mid A) = \frac{P_*(B \mid A)}{P_*(A \mid B)} \frac{P_*(C \mid B)}{P_*(B \mid C)}$$

$$\max \left[0, P_*(D \mid C) + P_*(B \mid C) + \frac{P_*(B \mid C)P_*(A \mid B)}{P_*(C \mid B)} - \frac{P_*(B \mid C)}{P_*(C \mid B)} - 1 \right]$$

and, due the generalised Bayes' theorem we presented in section 4 of this paper, we have:

$$\frac{P_*(C \mid A)}{P_*(A \mid C)} = \frac{P_*(B \mid A)}{P_*(A \mid B)} \frac{P_*(C \mid B)}{P_*(B \mid C)}$$

Q.E.D.

ANNEX 2

Proof of formula (13):

$$P(C \mid A \cup B) = \frac{\dfrac{(P(C \mid A)}{P(B \mid A)} + \dfrac{P(C \mid B)}{P(A \mid B)} - P(C \mid A \cap B)}{\dfrac{1}{P(B \mid A)} + \dfrac{1}{P(A \mid B)} - 1}$$

we have $P(X \cup Y) = P(X) + P(Y) - P(X \cap Y)$

$$P(C \mid A \cup B) = \frac{P[C \cap (A \cup B)]}{P(A \cup B)} = \frac{P[(C \cap A) \cap (C \cap B)]}{P(A) + P(B) - P(A \cap B)}$$

$$= \frac{P(C \cap A) + P(C \cap B) - P(A \cap B \cap C)}{P(A) + P(B) - P(A \cap B)}$$

thus, $P(C \mid A \cup B) = \dfrac{1}{\alpha} + \dfrac{1}{\beta} + \dfrac{1}{\gamma}$, with:

$$\alpha = \frac{P(A) + P(B) - P(A \cap B)}{P(C \cap A)} \quad ; \quad \beta = \frac{P(A) + P(B) - P(A \cap B)}{P(C \cap B)}$$

$$\gamma = \frac{P(A) + P(B) - P(A \cap B)}{P(A \cap B \cap C)}$$

then: $\alpha = \dfrac{P(B \mid A)}{P(C \mid A)} \left(\dfrac{1}{P(B \mid A)} + \dfrac{1}{P(A \mid B)} - 1 \right)$

The same way, we have: $\beta = \dfrac{P(A \mid B)}{P(C \mid B)} \left(\dfrac{1}{P(B \mid A)} + \dfrac{1}{P(A \mid B)} - 1 \right)$

And $\gamma = \dfrac{1}{P(C \mid A \cap B)} \left(\dfrac{1}{P(B \mid A)} + \dfrac{1}{P(A \mid B)} - 1 \right)$

Then, replacing α, β and γ by their value, we obtain the result.

Q.E.D.

ANNEX 3

Proof of the existence of a longest path between two nodes of Log N:
there exists a longest path between A_1 and A_n in
Log N over $(\Re \cup \{ + \infty \}, \max, +)$ if and only if each circuit of Log N has a
negative length, i.e., if and only if:

$$\forall i, j \in \,]\omega], \ \text{Log } d_{i, j} + \text{Log } d_{j, i} \leq 0.$$

But

$$\forall i, j \in \,]\omega], \ \text{Log } d_{i, j} + \text{Log } d_{j, i} = \text{Log } (d_{i, j} \cdot d_{j, i})$$

$$= \text{Log } \left(\frac{P_*(A_i \mid A_j)}{P^*(A_j \mid A_i)} \ \frac{P_*(A_j \mid A_i)}{P^*(A_i \mid A_j)} \right)$$

$$= \text{Log } \left(\frac{P_*(A_i \mid A_j)}{P^*(A_i \mid A_j)} \right) + \text{Log } \left(\frac{P_*(A_j \mid A_i)}{P^*(A_j \mid A_i)} \right)$$

And: $\forall i, j \in]\omega]$, $P*(A_i \mid A_j) \leq P^*(A_i \mid A_j)$,

so, $\forall i, j \in]\omega]$, $P*(A_i \mid A_j) / P^*(A_i \mid A_j) \leq 1$,

Then: $\forall i, j \in]\omega]$, Log $[P*(A_i \mid A_j) / P^*(A_i \mid A_j)] \leq 0$,

So: $\forall i, j \in]\omega]$, Log $\underline{d}_{i, j}$ + Log $\underline{d}_{j, i} \leq 0$.

Q.E.D.

7 Combining symbolic and numerical methods for reasoning under uncertainty

1 INTRODUCTION

Since its inception, artificial intelligence has seen a proliferation of paradigms for modelling belief and commonsense reasoning using uncertain and incomplete information. At their best, men and women are capable of great flexibility and subtlety in their ability to reason in diverse circumstances, and to adapt their reasoning style as situations and actions demand. A person may, for example: attach subjective, and revisable, measures of strength of belief to propositions; discount evidence from certain sources with respect to more credible sources; hold default assumptions until more specific information is available; evaluate the relative merits of competing hypotheses. In certain circumstances, it may even be that the framing of the problem under consideration needs to be revised. The diverse aspects of reasoning are being addressed in a piecemeal fashion with the many developments in numerical and symbolic reasoning. There are, for example, probabilistic methods for handling subjective belief, modal logics of belief, default logics, the Dempster-Shafer method of evidential reasoning, and fuzzy logics for handling vague and incomplete information. They all have their merits and rather than a continued retrenchment into their respective corners, recent years have seen increasing support for the development of an eclectic position in which a combination of calculi are used as appropriate [Saffiotti, 1988; Clark, 1990].

For the continued development of such an eclectic position to be effective, a framework for the combination of numerical and symbolic methods of reasoning needs to be identified. We propose here that the development of such a framework be approached by a slight change of perspective. Rather than modelling reasoning by a pre-identified network of probabilistic links between propositions or inference rules directly relating propositions, we suggest that a more general model of commonsense reasoning is that of identifying and appraising *arguments* using whatever sources of information are available or relevant to the problem at hand. For example, a simple default theory may be used to identify an argument in favour of Tweety being able to fly on the grounds that she is a bird. On more specific grounds that Tweety is an ostrich, we may also argue that Tweety is not able to fly. A comparison of the relative merits of the two arguments may then favour the final belief that Tweety is unable to fly is, most likely, the correct conclusion.

We define a very simple inference mechanism in which propositions are concluded with an appropriate qualifier and with the supporting grounds which initiated the argument for the proposition. Inference proceeds using information from whatever source is available. The qualifiers may be taken from a variety of dictionaries, allowing numeric and symbolic types of qualifier as appropriate to the method of inference being employed. If further inference requires information from sources using differing types of qualifiers, then 'combine' operators are used to merge the qualifiers. This may require a degradation of precision of the resulting qualifier to that of the least information intensive qualifier used in the inference.

This inference procedure will enable the identification of arguments supporting, or opposing, the truth of various propositions. We may then aggregate the qualifications of propositions by evaluating the relative merits of the arguments concerning each distinct proposition in order to provide a global qualification of that proposition. These global qualifications provide the basis for the final ordering of propositions that are regarded as competing hypotheses.

We give in the next section an informal motivation for a reasoning style based on argumentation. This is followed by an abstract model for the extended inference procedure. We then discuss the properties required of the aggregation operator. Following the use of a simple example to demonstrate the behaviour of an instance of the abstract model, we begin to develop the ideas of identifying and appraising arguments using information derived from various theories.

It should be emphasised that this is a purely informal presentation. Beginnings of a more formal and sound approach to this work can be found in [Fox et al., 1992].

2   MOTIVATION: A CASE STUDY IN MEDICAL DIAGNOSIS

One of the motivations for this work has been the need to provide a formal basis for the decision procedure employed in the Oxford System of Medicine. This is a comprehensive medical information system targeted for use in primary care [Fox et al., 1990a, b]. The requirement that the system covers the whole of general medicine and that the domain knowledge be reusable in the contexts of diagnosis, investigation, treatment and referral puts major demands on the technology that may be used to develop such a system.

Consider the problem of diagnosis. If building a rule-based system for medical diagnosis, one may try a rule such as:

If flat red spots *and* high temperature *then* measles.

Unfortunately, in medicine it is exceptional for diagnoses to be so clear cut. A rash of red spots may have a variety of causes (measles and systemic lupus erythematosus, sle, are two examples). We may have to be more specific about the type of spots. Koplick's spots are a pathognomonic indicant of measles. The additional indicant of a cough is also sufficient to diagnose measles. Unfortunately, Koplick's spots are only present for a small percentage of the period of infection by measles virus, and the cough may not necessarily be manifest. The patient may be suffering from measles, but the doctor may be unable to detect either of these symptoms during an examination. There are other indicants associated with measles, and any one of these indicants provides support for a diagnosis of measles, with the identification of Koplick's spots confirming this diagnosis.

If we model such reasoning with a rule-based system then the preconditions for a rule which unambiguously identified measles would have to be so specific that very few patients would present with the precise findings that would enable the rule to be fired. If the preconditions are weakened, then there may be many diseases which could account for the set of findings.

One alternative approach is to use a statistical model in which conditional probabilities are assigned to the links between diseases and findings [Lauritzen and Spiegelhalter, 1988]. As findings are confirmed, so the respective nodes in the statistical model are conditioned on. This will lead to a revision of the probabilities of the related diseases, from which the most likely disease given the current findings can be identified. There are two major problems with this approach:

1. For large branches of medicine, the required probability distributions are just not available. Assessing coherent and complete probability tables over such a large domain would be infeasible as there is often only very limited professional experience and statistical data available. The use of subjective probabilities to make predictions when they have been estimated on the basis of such limited experience would be highly suspect statistically. Their use may lead to an illusory degree of confidence in the probability value assigned to a decision option.

2. The use of probabilistic inference requires the preconstruction of the graph linking decision options (criteria) with observables or findings (predictors). However, the exact nature of these links may vary with context and the exact nature of the decision problem at hand. The need for a more flexible approach requires that the system be able to construct and revise the graph dynamically as information becomes available, and the goals of the problem at hand are identified.

A more general model is to provide rules for identifying links between predictors and criteria of interest in a given decision-making context. Such rules may be chained together to form an argument relating a predictor (e.g. red spots) to a relevant criterion (e.g. measles or SLE). Such an argument may have an associated *force*, qualifying the certainty of the criterion given that the line of reasoning (argumentation) is valid. It will also have an associated sign, depending on whether the argument supports the truth, or the falsity, of the criterion. We associate a qualifier with each criterion which contains a representation of this information. The predictor(s) are the grounds for the establishment of the argument.

We do not wish to say too much at this stage about the choice of qualifiers. However, examples of rules in a medical expert system based on these principles may include:

> finding(Finding)
> symptom(Disease, Finding)   R1
> (diagnosis(Disease), supported)

> finding(Finding)
> pathognomonic indicant(Disease, Finding)   R2
> (diagnosis(Disease), confirmed)

That is, if the specific case data includes the finding 'red spots' and 'red spots' are a symptom of measles, then we have a simple argument supporting the diagnosis of measles. But 'red spots' are also a symptom of sle, so R1 can also be used to identify an argument supporting sle. If 'Koplick's spots' are identified as a finding, and it is known that 'Koplick's spots' are a pathognomonic indicant of measles, then we may use R2 to identify a further argument which confirms the diagnosis of measles.

Usually, further arguments will just add further support, rather than confirmation, for specific diagnoses. We may take the qualifier *supported* as representing the information that we have identified a positive argument supporting the diagnosis of measles, say. As further information becomes available, more arguments will be identified which support, or oppose, the validity of specific diagnoses. In the absence of any confirming arguments, we then need to aggregate the qualifiers for each specific diagnosis. A very simple approach is to count the number of supporting arguments and subtract the number of negating arguments for each hypothesis. Although simple, such a counting of pros and cons (technically, an improper linear model with uniform weighting) is intuitive and remarkably effective [Dawes, 1979].

3   A LOGIC FOR IDENTIFYING ARGUMENTS

The overall aim is to obtain a logic in which propositions are augmented by qualifiers. The qualifiers are intended to summarise the degree of belief in, or commitment to, their associated proposition, together with the grounds for the argument leading to the proposition/qualifier pair.

Knowledge may be elicited from a source. Information may be presented by the source with an appropriate qualification. In addition, the reasoner will have a degree of confidence in the source which will attenuate this qualification. The qualification may be further attenuated as reasoning proceeds along a chain of inferences.

Knowledge may also be accumulated from several sources. The conjunction of this knowledge will be qualified by a combination of the individual qualifications.

The knowledge base is partitioned into various sources, each source X having an associated qualifier c_X expressing the confidence we have in the source. We may, for example, have a set of case specific data, knowledge elicited from various authorities, universally agreed knowledge and test results:

$$KB = Case \cup Authority_1 \cup ... \cup Authority_n \cup Universal \cup Test_1 \cup ... \cup Test_m$$

The formal language we shall use will be that of first-order logic augmented by a dictionary (or dictionaries) of qualifications. This will enable us to construct proposition/qualifier pairs (P,q). In the following, we will use upper case letters to represent propositions, and lower case letters for qualifiers.

We shall have a very similar notion of syntactic entailment as for first-order logic (FOL). However, the inductive definition of entailment will be augmented by rules for the combination of qualifiers as information is accumulated from different sources, and by rules for the attenuation of qualifiers as information is elicited from sources and as information is propagated along a chain of inferences.

In evaluating arguments, it will be useful to include information on the grounds G from which the argument has been derived. The grounds contain information on the initial facts upon which an argument is grounded and the theories that have been used to establish the argument. The intuition is that if a proposition can be derived from distinct grounds, and/or with different qualifiers, then these derivations should be regarded as separate 'arguments' supporting (or opposing) the proposition.

The knowledge base KB syntactically entails the triple (P,q,G) (i.e. KB $\vdash$ (P,q,G)) in the following cases:

1. KB $\vdash$ (P,q,G)

    if $\exists$ Source $\subseteq$ KB s.t. (P,t) $\in$ Source, confidence(Source) = c_S

    and q = attenuate_confidence(t,c_S)

2. if KB $\vdash$ (P,s,G_1)

    and KB $\vdash$ (Q,t,G_2)

    then KB $\vdash$ (P $\wedge$ Q, u, $G_1 \cup G_2$)

    where u = combine(s,t).

3. if KB $\vdash$ (P,s_1,G_1)

    and KB $\vdash$ (P $\Rightarrow$ (Q,t),s_2,G_2)

    then KB $\vdash$ (Q,v, $G_1 \cup G_2$)

    where u = attenuate_by_rule(t,s_1)

    and v = attenuate_confidence(u,s_2).

In the first case, the sentence P is obtained from the source Source by direct reference. We have not given any formal constraints on the grounds associated with P as yet. The grounds, G, may contain just a reference to P, if P is a proposition. Alternatively, if P is a more complex sentence, such as an inference rule, then G may also contain a label referring to the theory associated with the inference rule. As mentioned earlier, the qualification of the proposition by the source itself will be attenuated by the confidence in the source.

The conjunction of two sentences, in case (2), will be qualified by a combination of their individual qualifiers. For example, if the qualifiers were probabilities, the operator combine would be straightforward multiplication. For linguistic terms on which an ordering had been imposed, then a *min* operation may be appropriate.

In the third case, the rule P $\Rightarrow$ (Q,t) allows Q to be inferred with some qualification t, given P. If P has an associated qualification s1, this must attenuate the qualification of Q. The resulting qualification must, in turn, be attenuated by the confidence in the source of the rule s_2. When a proposition has been derived from a sequence of inferences, the final set of grounds associated with the proposition will in general contain information about the basic facts (predictors) which initiated the derivation, as well as those theories which have been used in its derivation.

There are a number of issues about the way in which we have generated the qualifiers for a derived proposition. In particular, the following remarks are worth highlighting:

> **Combine:** In this scheme the qualification of each proposition is attenuated by the confidence in the source before the resulting qualifications are combined. It may be that the aggregation of the

qualifications of the propositions and the confidences of the sources should not be split up in this way.

attenuate_: As above, we have split the aggregation of qualification into two components; attenuate_confidence and attenuate_by_rule. Possibly this should not be done. There is, also, no *a priori* reason why attenuate_confidence and attenuate_by_rule should not correspond to the same operation. But we allow the possibility of differing operations to be considered.

4   AGGREGATION OF QUALIFIERS

A proposition may be inferred from a variety of different reasoning paths ('arguments'). As will be discussed more fully later, if we infer the same proposition P with different qualifications, or with the same qualifications but differing grounds, then we consider these as distinct arguments for P.

That is, if

$$KB \vdash (P,q_1,G_1)$$

and

$$KB \vdash (P,q_2,G_2)$$

$$\text{where } q_1 \neq q_2 \text{ or, } q_1 = q_2 \text{ and } G_1 \neq G_2$$

then there are two distinct arguments for P. It should again be emphasised that the grounds G_1 and G_2 are sets which may contain information concerning the predictors which initiated the argument, as well as information on the theories used in developing the argument. Thus, for example, distinct arguments would be associated with a proposition if the same predictors have been used to derive the proposition, but using distinct theories.

Once two or more distinct arguments for a proposition P have been identified, the associated qualifications q_i will need to be aggregated to form a global qualification 'q' of P. To enable the revision of 'q' as new arguments are identified, or as invalidated arguments are retracted, an operator for the incremental aggregation of qualifiers is proposed. Suppose the global qualification of P is 'q'. If a new argument i is identified from which P is inferred with qualification q_i, then the qualification 'q' should be revised to form q', where

$$q' = agg(q,q_i)$$

In the section on 'motivation' we suggested the use of a very simple aggregation operator in which the opposing arguments were counted, and this number subtracted from the number of supporting arguments. In the current implementation of the Oxford System of Medicine, the counting of supporting arguments is overruled by the identification of "confirming" or "eliminating" arguments. There are a variety of aggregation operators which we may use for *agg* and the specific choice will depend on the dictionary of qualifiers being used and may depend on the nature of the application under consideration. However, it is possible to state some general requirements which the chosen operator should satisfy [Ginsberg, 1984]:

1. It should be commutative and associative. The final result should be independent of the order in which the arguments are identified and in which the qualifiers are aggregated.

2. Accumulating a qualifier expressing total ignorance should have no effect on the aggregation.

3. If using numerical qualifiers, the operation should reduce to the usual combination for point probabilities.

4. No non-monotonic rule can outweigh a logical certainty.

5. The combination of 'certainly believed' and 'certainly disbelieved' is undefined.

6. Combination should be invertible. We may wish to be able to retract a qualification should an argument become invalidated.

5   A SIMPLE EXAMPLE

The inference rules used in our model have a slightly different meaning to those expressed in classical logical inference. Rather than looking for strict logical links, or probabilistic links between items in the domain of interest, it is intended that the inference rules be used to establish connections between items in the knowledge domain in a given context. However, in this section we will compare our treatment of a classic example with a more conventional treatment using default logic. Default rules are of the form

$$\frac{A:B}{C}$$

which may be read as: if the precondition A is satisfied, and it is consistent to believe B, then conclude C. Such rules are non-monotonic, as with the identification of new information the assumption of B may be invalidated, requiring the conclusion of C from this rule to be retracted. A simple example of the use of such a rule in an expert system may be in a system for identifying possible recipients for a mailshot. If the requirement is to target retired people, it is reasonably safe to assume that if someone is over 65 then he or she will be retired:

$$\frac{age(X) > 65 : retired(X)}{retired(X)}$$

In those cases where it is known through some other source that they are not retired, this rule will be blocked.

A textbook use of default logic is in the following simple example. It is known that birds are usually able to fly. It is also known that penguins usually do not fly. We have the following rules:

$$\frac{bird(X) : flies(X)}{flies(X)} \tag{1}$$

$$\frac{penguin(X)}{bird(X)} \tag{2}$$

$$\frac{penguin(X) : not\ flies(X)}{not\ flies(X)} \tag{3}$$

If it is known that Tweety is a bird, we may use the first rule to establish that *flies(Tweety)* by default. If we know that Tweety is a penguin (*penguin(Tweety)*) a difficulty arises with the problem framed in this way with no additional information. We may use rule 2 to infer with certainty *bird(Tweety)*. We may now use this information and apply the default rule 1 to conclude *flies(Tweety)*. Knowing *flies(Tweety)* will block the application of rule 3 (it would not be consistent to assume *not flies(Tweety)*). On the other hand, were we to apply the default rule (3) before rule (1) we would infer *not flies(Tweety)* which would block the application of rule (1). So we may conclude either *flies(Tweety)* or *not flies(Tweety)*, but in the absence of any further constraints we are not able to choose between the two possibilities.

One possible approach to discriminating between these two possible extensions[1] to the default theory is to introduce a priority ordering on the applicability of the default rules based on grounds of specificity [Poole, 1985; Touretzky, 1984]. Here, *penguin(Tweety)* is regarded as more specific information than *bird(Tweety)* so we will attempt to apply rule (3) before the application of rule (1). This gives a unique extension in which it is concluded that Tweety does not fly.

---

1. Loosely, an extension of a default theory is the set of all facts which may be consistently derived from the theory.

In our framework, we also regard rule (2) as a strict inference:

$$penguin(X) \Rightarrow (bird(X), true) \tag{A1}$$

We then say that the identification of something as a bird is an argument in favour of it flying, although not categorical:

$$bird(X) \Rightarrow (flies(X), possible) \tag{A2}$$

In fact our resident expert, whom we trust explicitly, is sure that being a penguin is an excluding argument for something flying:

$$penguin(X) \Rightarrow (flies(X), false) \tag{A3}$$

For simplicity we are assuming that all our sources are reliable, and so ignore the attenuation of the qualifications by the confidences in the sources. Suppose we know that Tweety is a penguin. Using rule (A1) we may conclude (*bird(Tweety)*, *true*, *{penguin(Tweety)}*). The dictionary of qualifiers used here includes the symbolic terms false, possible, true. An ordering may be placed on the support represented by the qualifier for its associated proposition, where false < possible < true. Using a simple 'min' operator for attenuate_by_rule we then apply rule (A2) to conclude

$$(flies(Tweety), possible, \{penguin(Tweety)\})$$

We have identified an argument grounded in the fact *penguin(Tweety)* which supports the conclusion that Tweety flies, although it is not categoric. On the other hand, we may apply rule (A3) to conclude

$$(flies(Tweety), false, \{penguin(Tweety)\}).$$

The grounds for these two conclusions are the same, but the qualifiers differ, so we regard them as distinct arguments concerning the ability of Tweety to fly. The inference engine will draw all possible conclusions, so to obtain the final result we must aggregate the two qualifications using the operator agg to produce the global qualification for *flies(Tweety)*. We will not say much about the instance of agg that is used here, except that it satisfies requirement (4) of the previous section; no non-monotonic rule can outweigh a logical certainty. That is, 'false' overrides 'possible' and we obtain the final result

$$(flies(Tweety), false)$$

Were we less sure about the universality of penguins not flying, a less categorical qualifier would have been attached to the conclusion of (A3). This would, in turn, have led to a modification of the concluding qualification. That is, *agg* would embody a scheme for 'weighing up' the arguments for and against Tweety flying.

6 COMBINING NUMERIC AND SYMBOLIC QUALIFIERS

We have said little so far concerning the combination of symbolic and numerical methods. The knowledge base is partitioned into various sources; authorities, test data, universal knowledge, etc. Each source will present information with an appropriate qualification, and the sources themselves may have an appropriate qualification reflecting a degree of confidence in the source. For example, a medical expert system may be interfaced to a patient monitoring system. A Back End Manager (BEM) [Southwick et al., 1990] is used to interface the KBS to the patient monitoring application in such a way that a query from the KBS is converted to the appropriate commands for the application. The result will then be returned to the KBS as a simple fact, as if looked up in a database of test facts, with an uncertainty figure obtained from a statistical analysis of the measurements that have been performed.

On the other hand, an 'Authority' partition of the database may return a proposition with, perhaps, a Dempster-Shafer belief mass assigned to it [Shafer, 1976]. The Dempster-Shafer theory of belief functions is a numerical uncertainty handling technique which differs from the more classical Bayesian treatment in a number of ways. Perhaps the most significant difference is that it allows an expression of ignorance. A belief mass may be assigned to a set of propositions if one cannot differentiate further between the elements of the set; I may be 80% sure that the murderer was one of Peter, Paul or Mary, but quite unable to say any more than that. In the Dempster-Shafer approach, a belief mass of 0.8 would be assigned to the set {Peter, Paul, Mary}. The Dempster rule of combination then allows belief to be transferred to appropriate subsets of {Peter, Paul, Mary} from that assigned to non-disjoint sets by other sources of evidence. Suppose there is now an inference rule which requires the conjunction of information from the Test source (obtained as a fact and an associated probability) and an Authority (obtained as a fact and an associated belief mass). According to our definition of entailment, the operator *combine* is used to generate the qualification of the conjunction from the two individual qualifiers. But the qualifiers are of two different types, so one or other of them must undergo some transformation as part of the combine operation. In this particular case, the choice is quite straightforward. [Smets, 1989] offers a "pignistic transformation" by which probability assignments can be obtained from the transferable belief model. The resulting probabilities may then be multiplied together to give the qualifier of the conjunction.

A more usual presentation of the Test result would be as a value with an associated standard deviation. The actual value of the standard deviation would actually have little influence in evaluating the force of an argument grounded on this test result, providing it was within specification for the instrumentation in use. So in this case one could reasonably qualify the result with *confirmed*. In addition, unless one had grounds to suspect the reliability of the instrument, there would be no attenuation of this qualification by the confidence in the source. So, assuming the standard deviation is within specification and we are using instrumentation we are confident in, then we may receive a test result:

(finding('blood calcium level = 3.82 mmol/l'), confirmed).

Relevant facts for this case will include:

symptom('bony metastasis', 'raised blood calcium')
symptom(hypercalcaemia, 'raised blood calcium')
symptom(dehydration, 'raised blood calcium')

These symptoms can be used to generate a number of ground instances of rule R1 given earlier. For example:

finding('raised blood calcium')
symptom('bony metastasis', 'raised blood calcium')
(diagnosis('bony metastasis'), supported)

We now need to obtain a qualification for *finding('raised blood calcium')* based on the crisp evaluation of the blood calcium level. Again, there is a technology available to enable us to do this, using the ideas of fuzzy set theory [Zadeh, 1965]. This would require the definition of a membership function for the concept *'raised blood calcium'* to enable an assessment to be made of the degree of compatibility of the value of 3.82 mmol/l with the concept. We would then obtain a fuzzy quantifier for the antecedent of the above rule, which would be attenuated, using the operator *attenuate_confidence*, by the linguistic qualifier supported to obtain the final qualification of the conclusion *diagnosis('bony metastasis')*. This again requires a translation of one of the two qualifiers, but here, also, one may call on an existing body of work on the representation of linguistic qualifiers using fuzzy set theory [Godo et al., 1989] and fuzzy modus ponens [Baldwin, 1979] to enable us to generate the final qualification.

It is also possible that one of the partitions of the database would consist of a default theory, embodying a set of inferences which it may be useful to make in a given context, in the absence of more complete information. For example, a woman of child-bearing age missing periods would lead to a default assumption of pregnancy. The 'default authority' would in this case present the fact *finding(pregnant)*, but the grounds for the finding would refer to the default theory used as well as the initial facts from which the conclusion has been drawn; {child_bearing_age, missed_periods, default}. If the problem under consideration is identification of an appropriate investigation for chest pain, then this finding would provide grounds for a strong argument against chest X-ray. But the fact that this conclusion is founded on a default assumption needs to be propagated through the argument. The difficulty here is to suggest a convincing translation scheme which would enable the default tag to be attenuated by, or combined with, a qualifier of a different type. In fact, there is a strong case for not aggregating or otherwise obscuring this information from the user, for if a chest X-ray is otherwise strongly supported, then confirmation or otherwise of pregnancy should be sought before it is ruled out on the grounds of this default assumption. For these reasons, we keep the information on the theories used separate (in the set of grounds) to the qualifiers. So in this particular case the grounds are not only used to distinguish between different arguments, but also contain information which is of use in evaluating and aggregating the different arguments for a proposition. We have asserted in the previous section that a default should be overruled by a logical certainty, but would emphasise again that the intercomparison between degrees of belief in default conclusions, and conclusions qualified by some other measure of belief, is by no means clear cut.

7   DISCUSSION

We have described an abstract framework for identifying and evaluating arguments relating predictors to criteria of interest in a decision-making context. The inference engine has available to it a variety of sources of information from which it may draw facts with an associated qualification. These facts are the predictors which form the grounds of arguments. The inference engine will then construct the arguments using inference rules which establish links between the predictors and the criteria of interest; for example, linking symptoms to diseases, general criteria to more specific criteria. Symbolic or numeric qualifiers are propagated through the links as they are established which summarise the information concerning the 'force' of the arguments. One simple way of evaluating the relative merits of competing criteria is to add up the number of supporting, and subtract the number of opposing, arguments for each criterion. We suggest that should an argument identify the truth or the falsehood of a proposition as a logical certainty, then this should override any defeasible inference.

We have not provided any guidance here as to how the relevant sources in a given decision-making context may be identified. It need not necessarily be the case that all available sources should be used for a given problem. In addition, there may be grounds for calling on extra sources as the decision process progresses. All we have provided here is a very abstract model in which all sources are available, and inference proceeds freely with no constraints on the domain of the conclusions drawn, and no control or external guidance of the inference procedure. An important refinement of this model would be to enable the system to critique the conclusions drawn and modify its behaviour appropriately. For example, to conclude that it has insufficient information available to it to be able to identify reliably a most likely disease, and identify and call upon appropriate test results to enable it to disambiguate the possible outcomes.

Different arguments will, in general, have differing degrees of support for, or against, specific decision options. We have made some suggestions as to how numerical and symbolic qualifiers may be integrated to produce a qualifier representing the 'force' of a specific argument. As regards aggregating these qualifiers to produce an overall measure of confidence, we have suggested a slightly modified use of an improper linear model with uniform weighting. Further work is under way to identify dictionaries of qualifiers which will enable a more optimal weighting of the respective arguments.

8   CONCLUSIONS

Reasoning under uncertainty is a problem with many putative solutions. They each capture different aspects of uncertain reasoning and so there is a strong case for identifying a framework within which the various approaches may be loosely coupled. The approach we have taken here is to use whichever uncertainty calculus is appropriate to solve certain sub-problems in the task at hand. The data so obtained may then be used as the grounds for arguments which may be dynamically generated, supporting, or opposing, the criteria of interest. We have so far identified some fairly general rules to 'weigh' the relative merits of various arguments whose force may be qualified using symbolic or numerical terms.

The abstract model we have described here is at a very early stage in its development and there is scope for extensive refinement of the very simple instances of various aspects of the model which we have used for illustration in this paper. Our thesis is that it provides:

- a more flexible model than any one of the individual calculi currently in vogue, in which the knowledge base may be used in a variety of decision-making contexts without modification.
- a more robust model that is better able to cope with the absence of statistical data than the existing numerical uncertainty calculi.

- a framework in which the qualifiers may be instantiated to quite complex structures which will be of value in explanation and critiquing of the conclusions drawn.

Most of the ideas discussed in this paper do need further development. However, our experience in developing knowledge based systems along the lines identified here is very supportive of the above thesis.

9   ACKNOWLEDGEMENTS

We would like to thank all our colleagues in the Biomedical Computing Unit for many useful discussions on this work, but especially Saki Hajnal, Dominic Clark, Andrzej Glowinski and Mirko Dohnal. This work has received an added stimulus with our involvement in and support from the Esprit Basic Research Programme 3085, DRUMS.

P. Krause is supported under the SERC project 1822: a Formal Basis for Decision Support Systems. Our thanks also to Mike Clarke of Queen Mary College who is involved in this project with us.

REFERENCES

Baldwin, J.A. (1979) A new approach to approximate reasoning using fuzzy logic, Fuzzy Sets and Systems, 2, pp. 309–325.

Clark, D.A. (1990) Numerical and symbolic approaches to uncertainty management in AI, Artificial Intelligence Review, 4, pp. 109–146.

Dawes, R.M. (1979) The robust beauty of improper linear models in decision making, American Psychologist, 34, pp. 571–582.

Fox, J., Krause, P.J. and Ambler, S. (1992) Arguments, contradictions and practical reasoning, Proc. ECAI 92, Vienna, Austria, pp. 623–627.

Fox, J., Glowinski, A.J., Gordon, C., Hajnal, S.J. and O'Neil, M.J. (1990a) Logic engineering for knowledge engineering: design and implementation of the Oxford System of Medicine, Artificial Intelligence in Medicine, 2, pp. 323–339.

Fox, J., Clark, D.A., Glowinski, A.J. and O'Neil, M.J. (1990b) Using predicate logic to integrate qualitative reasoning and classical decision theory, IEEE Trans. on Systems, Man, and Cybernetics, 20, pp. 347–357.

Ginsberg, M.L. (1984) Non-monotonic reasoning using Dempster's rule, Proc. AAAI-84, Austin, Texas, pp. 126–129.

Godo, L., Lopez de Mantaras, R., Sierra, C. and Verdaguer, L. (1989) MILORD: the architecture and management of linguistically expressed uncertainty, International Journal of Intelligent Systems, 4, pp. 471–501.

Lauritzen, S.L. and Spiegelhalter, D.J. (1988) Local computations with probabilities on graphical structures and their application to expert systems, J. R. Statist. Soc. B., 50, pp. 157–224.

Poole, D.L. (1985) On the comparison of theories: preferring the most specific explanation, Proc. IJCAI 9, Los Angeles, pp. 144–147.

Saffiotti, A. (1988) An AI view of the treatment of uncertainty, Knowledge Engineering Review, 2, pp. 75–98.

Smets, P. (1989) Constructing the pignistic probability function in a context of uncertainty, Procs. of the Fifth Workshop on Uncertainty in AI, Windsor, Canada, pp. 319–326.

Touretzky, D.S. (1984) Implicit Ordering of Defaults in Inheritance Systems, Proc. AAAI-84, Austin, Texas, pp. 322–325.

Zadeh, L.A. (1965) Fuzzy Sets, Inform. Contr., 8, pp. 338–353.

8 Computationally intensive methods in the design of experiments

A. C. Atkinson
Department of Statistical and Mathematical Sciences,
London School of Economics

1 INTRODUCTION

The theory of the optimum design of experiments provides a powerful collection of general techniques for the definition and construction of designs for a wide variety of standard and non-standard purposes. Examples of both will be given in this paper. Construction of the designs can raise interesting optimisation problems and it is on this aspect that the paper concentrates.

The central theoretical result of optimum experimental design, the General Equivalence Theorem (Kiefer and Wolfowitz, 1960), holds for continuous or approximate designs. In these designs the dependence of the optimum design on the number of trials is removed by considering an asymptotic design measure. However, designs which are to be used must have an integer number of trials. Such designs are called exact and several algorithms for their construction have been described in the statistical literature. However, the construction of an exact design can be formulated as a problem in combinatorial optimisation, for which one potential algorithm is simulated annealing. The purpose of the present paper is to summarise some work on the use of pattern-search algorithms and of simulated annealing in the construction of exact experimental designs.

The emphasis in the paper is on D-optimality, which is introduced in section 2, where the distinction is made between exact and continuous designs. The application of one pattern-search algorithm to the construction of response surface designs is described in section 3. Section 4 mainly reports the use of simulated annealing for generation of a nonlinear design, although some work on response surface designs is noted. In addition to references to related work, the last section mentions a use of branch and bound for the construction of exact designs.

2   CONTINUOUS AND EXACT DESIGNS

In the linear model

$$E(Y) = F\beta \tag{1}$$

with F an $N \times p$ extended design matrix, the ith row of F is $f^T(x_i)$, a function of m factors x. In the response surface example of this section $f(x)$ is a second-order polynomial. The information matrix for $\hat{\beta}$, the least squares estimate of β, is F^TF, with the covariance matrix of $\hat{\beta}$ given by $\sigma^2(F^TF)^{-1}$.

The exact experimental design problem is to choose N not necessarily distinct values of x_i, $i = 1, ..., N$, from the experimental region χ to make $(F^TF)^{-1}$ small or, equivalently, F^TF large. For D-optimum designs the values are chosen to maximise

$$|M(N)| = |F^TF| \tag{2}$$

so that the generalised variance of the parameter estimates is minimised. The D-optimum design will thus minimise the volume of the normal theory confidence ellipsoid for β for any specified content.

Let the exact design put r_i observations at the point x_i. The design can be written as a measure ξ_N which puts mass r_i/N at x_i, $i = 1, ..., N_1$, where N_1 is the number of distinct design points and the r_i are integers. Removal of the integer restriction yields the continuous design measure ξ.

The D-optimum continuous design ξ^* will have at least p points of support. As the following example shows, this design can be very different from the exact D-optimum design ξ_N^*, particularly when N is close to p.

Example 1. Second-order response surface in two factors
The model is

$$Y = \beta_0 + \beta_1 x_1 + \beta_2 x_2 + \beta_{11} x_1^2 + \beta_{22} x_2^2 + \beta_{12} x_1 x_2 + \varepsilon . \tag{3}$$

The independent errors ε have constant variance σ^2. There are $m = 2$ factors and $p = 6$ parameters.

The D-optimum design depends on the experimental region χ. In this, and other, examples, we take χ to be a square so scaled that the vertices of the region are $(\pm 1, \pm 1)$. The optimum continuous design ξ^* is found, typically by a combination of algebra and of numerical search over χ, to have design weights

      0.1458 at 4 corner points $(\pm 1, \pm 1)$
      0.0802 at 4 centres of sides $(0, \pm 1; \pm 1, 0)$
      0.0960 at the centre point $(0, 0)$ $\tag{4}$

The General Equivalence Theorem can be used to prove that this is the D-optimum continuous design. The condition is that the variance of the predicted response from (3) has its maximum value over χ at the design points, in this case the points of the 3^2 factorial. At these points the variance is, in general, equal to p.

A good integer approximation to the continuous design consists of the 3^2 factorial with the corner points replicated. For N = 13 this provides a very satisfactory exact design, even though it cannot be proved that it is best for this value of N. For other values of N it is not even true that the best designs consist solely of fractions or replicates of the 3^2 factorial.

Box and Draper (1971) use straightforward function maximisation to find exact D-optimum designs for second-order models in m = 2 and 3 factors with χ a square or cube. When, as in our example, m = 2 the search for exact optimum designs requires a constrained search in 2N dimensons. The exact optimum designs given by Box and Draper for N = 6 to 9 are:

N = 6. (–1, –1), (1, –1), (–1, 1), (–α, –α), (1, 3α), (3α, 1),

where $\alpha = (4 - \sqrt{13})/3$. Equally optimum designs are obtained by rotation of this design through $\frac{\pi}{2}$, π or $\frac{3\pi}{2}$

N = 7. (±1, ±1), (–0.092, 0.092), (1, –0.067), (0.067, –1)
N = 8. (±1, ±1), (1, 0), (0.082, 1), (0.082, –1), (–0.215, 0)
N = 9. The 3^2 factorial with levels –1, 0 and 1

Apart from the design for N = 6, the designs are very close to fractions of the 3^2 factorial. Even the design for N = 6 contains three such points.

As the dimension of the problem and the number of factors increase, the time needed to search over the continuous region for the exact design rapidly becomes unacceptable. Following the indication of results such as those of Box and Draper, the search over the continuous region χ is often replaced by a search over a list of candidate points. The list, usually a coarse grid in the experimental region, frequently includes the points of the D-optimum continuous design. In the example above the list might well consist of only the 9 points of the 3^2 factorial. Use of the finer grid of the 5^2 factorial typically has no beneficial effect. The design problem of Example 1 is then the combinatorial one of choosing the N out of the available nine points which maximise |M(N)|. In general the problem is that of selecting N points out of a list of N_c candidate points. Since replication is allowed, the selection is with replacement.

Replacement of optimisation over χ by a search over the list of candidate points greatly simplifies the search for optimum exact designs. There are also other advantages, the chief of which is that many disparate design problems are reduced to a common optimisation structure. Whether the variables are quantitative or qualitative factors or mixture variables, the search reduces to selecting points from a list of length N_C. The incorporation of non-regular or restricted regions, or of several types of variable, introduces no difficulties. Of course, the choice of the list of candidate points is crucial. The list must contain sufficient points to support a good approximation to the exact optimum design over χ. But, in cases of doubt, the adjustment algorithm described at the end of the next section, which searches away from the list of candidate points, can be used to check that a good design has been found.

3   PATTERN-SEARCH METHODS

3.1   Introduction

In this section we discuss methods for finding an exact optimum design by searching over a list of candidate points. A relatively detailed description of one algorithm, the KL-exchange, is given in section 3.2. The adjustment algorithm, for exploring the neighbourhood of a design found by search over the list of candidate points, is described in section 3.3.

Numerical algorithms for the construction of exact D-optimum designs by searching over a list of N_C candidate points customarily involve three phases:

1. Generation of a starting design of $N_0 < N$ trials;
2. Sequential augmentation of the starting design to give an initial N-trial design;
3. Improvement of the N-trial design by exchange.

In general the algorithms are attempting to find the maximum of a surface with many local extrema. Many of the algorithms cannot be guaranteed to find anything more than a local optimum. The probability of finding the global optimum can be increased by repeating the search several times from different starting designs, the generation of which often includes a random component. The probability of finding the global optimum can also be increased by the use of a more thorough search algorithm for improvement of the initial design. With a long list of candidate points and several model parameters, complicated search algorithms can readily consume appreciable computer time and space. The problem is discussed by Galil and Kiefer (1980). For restricted resources, there needs to be a balance between the number of starting designs and the complexity of the search algorithm. The procedure described in section 3.2 uses a simple search, but requires several starts or 'tries' (Mitchell, 1974) to have a reasonable chance of locating the best design, or one close to it.

The initial design of size N is constructed sequentially from a starting design of size N_0, by the addition of points chosen to give the maximum increase in value of the determinant at each stage. Let the determinant for a design of size n < N be $|M(n)| = |F^T F|$. Addition of the point x_1 yields the new determinant

$$|M(n+1)| = |F^T F + f(x_1) f^T(x_1)| \tag{5}$$

It is not however necessary to calculate the determinant in (5) for every candidate point, since the relationship

$$|F^T F + f(x_1) f^T(x_1)| = |F^T F| \{1 + f(x_1) (F^T F)^{-1} f(x_1)\} \tag{6}$$

(for example, Rao, 1965, p. 29), shows that addition of that point for which the variance of the predicted response is maximum will lead to the greatest increase in the determinant. Improvement of the design in the third of the three phases listed above is made by the exchange of points between the design and the candidate list. The extension of (6) to the exchange of points x_k from the design and x_1 from the list is given by Fedorov (1972, p. 164), Cook and Nachtsheim (1980) and by Atkinson and Donev (1992, eqn 15.3). The choice of the points x_k and x_1 then depends on the variance of the predicted response at these points, the determinant of the information matrix and on the values of elements of its inverse. The search strategy is determined by the algorithm. The computer implementation of these formulas requires care: updating the design and the inverse of its information matrix, in addition to recalculation of the variances at the design points, can consume computer time and space. Some advice is given by Galil and Kiefer (1980).

3.2 The KL Exchange Algorithm

As the exchange algorithms for exact designs are finding local optima of functions with many extrema, improvement can come from an increased number of starting designs as well as from more precise identification of local optima. Experience suggests that, for fixed computational cost, there are benefits from a proper balance between the number of tries and the elaborateness of each search. The original exchange algorithm suggested by Fedorov (1972, p. 164) evaluates the effect of exchanging all possible pairs of points between the design and the candidate list. The algorithm is made slow by the large number of points to be considered at each iteration (a maximum of $N(N_c - 1)$ in the absence of replication in the design) and by the need to follow each successful exchange by updating the design, the covariance matrix $M^{-1}(\xi)$ and the variance of the predicted values at the design and candidate points. The thoroughness of the search contributes to the success of the algorithm. However, the search can be made faster by noting that the points most likely to be exchanged are design points with relatively low variance of the predicted response and candidate points for which the variance is relatively high. This idea underlies the KL exchange and its extension to blocking, called BLKL, by Atkinson and Donev (1989).

The algorithm passes through the three phases mentioned above of the generation of a starting design, followed by its augmentation and improvement. Sometimes there may be points which the experimenter wishes to include in the design. The purpose might be to check the model, or they might represent data already available. The first phase starts with q_1 ($q_1 \geq 0$) such points. The random start to the search for the optimum comes from choosing q_2 points at random from the candidate set, where q_2 is itself a randomly chosen integer $0 \leq q_2 \leq \min (N - q_1, [p/2])$, where [a] is the integer part of a.

The initial N-trial design is completed by sequential addition of those $N - (q_1 + q_2)$ points which give maximum increase to the determinant of the information matrix. For $N < p$ the design will be singular and is regularised by replacement of $F^T F$ by $F^T F + \varepsilon I_p$, where ε is a small number, typically between 10^{-4} and 10^{-6} (Vuchkov, 1977). If the design is to be laid out in blocks, the search for the next design point is confined to those parts of the candidate set corresponding to non-full blocks.

In the third phase the exchange of points x_k from the design and x_l from the candidate list is considered. As in other algorithms of the exchange type, that exchange is performed which leads to the greatest increase in the determinant of the information matrix. The algorithm terminates when there is no longer any exchange which would increase the determinant. The points x_k and x_l considered for exchange are determined by parameters K and L such that

$$1 \leq k \leq K \leq N$$

and

$$1 \leq 1 \leq L \leq N_c - 1$$

The point x_k is that with the kth lowest variance of prediction among the N design points and x_l has the lth highest variance among the N_c candidate points. If blocking is required, the orderings of points are over each block and exchanges are limited to pairs within the same block. Whether blocking is required or not, the q_1 points added at the beginning of the starting procedure are not considered for exchange.

When $K = N$ and $L = N_c - 1$, the KL exchange coincides with Fedorov's procedure. However, by choosing $K < N$ and $L < N_c - 1$ the number of pairs of points to be considered at each iteration is decreased. Although this must diminish the probability of finding the best possible exact design at each try, the decrease can be made negligible if K and L are properly chosen. The advantage is the decrease in computational time.

The best values of K and L depend, amongst other variables, on the number of factors, degrees of freedom for error $v = N - p$ and the number of candidate points N_c. For example, when $v = 0$, the variance of the predicted response at all design points is the same: there is then no justification for taking K less than N. However as v increases, the ratio K/N should decrease. The best value of L increases with the size of the problem, but never exceeded $N_c/2$ in the examples considered in Donev (1988). In most cases values of K and L much smaller than these limits were sufficient, particularly if the number of tries is high. In an example reported in detail by Donev (1988) the unmodified Fedorov algorithm was used for repeated tries on two test problems in order to find the values of K and L required so that the optimum exchange was always made. In none of the tries would taking K or L equal 1 have yielded the optimum exchange – usually much larger values were necessary.

Example 2. Second-order response surface with a single qualitative factor

In addition to the quantitative factors of the response surface of Example 1, the response may depend on one or more qualitative factors. Designs for models containing both kind of factor have not been much studied. Kurotschka (1981) gave the theory for D-optimum continuous designs. Exact designs are calculated by Atkinson and Donev (1989) using the algorithms described in this section.

As an example consider the model

$$E(Y) = \sum_{i=1}^{B} \alpha_i e_i + \beta_1 x_1 + \beta_2 x_2 + \beta_{11} x_1^2 + \beta_{22} x_2^2 + \beta_{12} x_1 x_2 \qquad (3)$$

where e_i is an indicator variable for the B levels of the qualitative factor. In (7) the response surface moves up and down according to the level of the qualitative factor, which does not interact with the quantitative factors. In a technological experiment this could be the type of apparatus or the batch of raw material.

The continuous D-optimum design repeats the design (4) at each level of the qualitative factor. Even repetition of the 13-trial exact design at each level produces a design in which N is very much greater than p. For values of N near p, the optimum designs of course have a very different structure. For example, when $N = 9$ and the qualitative variable is at three levels, so that p

= 8, the design found by searching over the points of the 3^2 factorial at each level is:

Qualitative Factor	Quantitative Factors
1	(–1, –1), (0, 0), (1, –1)
2	(1, –1), (–1, 0), (1, 1)
3	(0, –1), (1, 0), (–1, 1). (8)

Permutations of the levels of the qualitative factor do not alter this design.

Although the structure of (8) is very different from that of the D-optimum continuous design, the D-efficiency, defined as $[|M (\xi_N)|/|M(xi^*)|]^{1/p}$, is high, 90.38. There are several interesting features of the design. Although the nine trials have been divided equally between the three levels of the qualitative variable, this is not a general feature of such designs, which tend towards a division providing a structured pattern at each level. In the absence of the qualitative factor, the D-optimum exact design for N = 9 is the 3^2 factorial. But the projection of (8) onto one level by ignoring the qualitative factor does not yield the factorial design. Finally, if the design is to be blocked, the number of trials at each level of the qualitative factor is specified. Fuller details and numerous examples are given by Atkinson and Donev (1989) and by Cook and Nachtsheim (1989), where the emphasis is on the blocking of designs.

3.3   An Adjustment Algorithm

The KL-exchange searches over a list of candidate points. For quantitative factors the list often consists of a coarse grid, such as the points of a 3^m factorial. But, as Example 1 showed, even if these comprise the points of support of the optimum continuous design, they may not support the optimum exact design. In this section a description is given of the adjustment algorithm, which searches away from the candidate list in the neighbourhood of a good exact design.

As a result of applying the KL-exchange algorithm a design is obtained at a local optimum for the given candidate set. The adjustment algorithm is a method of finding this local optimum more precisely by adjusting the design points. At each of the N points of the proposed exact design the effect is calculated of moving the design point a small amount along each factor axis. If an increase is possible, the single point for which it is greatest is changed and the process repeated until progress ceases. At the most there are 2mN perturbations per stage, less if any of the design points are on the boundary of χ, or if there is any replication in the design.

Application of the algorithm to exact designs for the second-order response surface of Example 1 produces the designs of Box and Draper from fractions of the 3^2 factorial. For Example 2 the main effect of the adjustment algorithm on design (8) is to move the centre point in the direction of increasing x_2, yielding a D-efficiency of 91.42%. The two designs are shown in figure 4 of Atkinson and Donev (1989). The paper also gives details of other examples which confirm the observation that the effect of the adjustment algorithm is greatest when N is equal to, or just greater than, p.

The adjustment algorithm is very simple. More complicated search strategies are, of course, possible. But limited experience suggests that these add computational complexity without yielding improved designs. Although the search is not particularly efficient, it is only employed on the single best design found by the exchange algorithm. After, for example, 100 tries of a complicated search, the computational efficiency of the final single search using the adjustment algorithm is not critical. The search is however worthwhile, for example for blocked response surfaces designs with few trials per block, where the number of trials and parameters are comparable.

4   SIMULATED ANNEALING

Simulated annealing algorithms are a general class of optimisation procedures which perform well in finding the global extremum of a function with many local extrema. The method is therefore an interesting alternative to standard algorithms for the construction of optimum designs, such as those of section 3. In this section a review is given of the literature on the use of simulated annealing for the calculation of optimum designs. The treatment follows that of Bohachevsky et al. (1986).

Let ϕ be the function to be minimised. Consider a step from x_0, where the value is ϕ_0, to x_1 with function value ϕ_1. This step is accepted with probability p where:

$$
\begin{aligned}
p &= 1 && (\Delta\phi = \phi_1 - \phi_0 \leq 0) \\
p &= \exp(-\beta\Delta\phi) && (\Delta\phi > 0)
\end{aligned}
\tag{9}
$$

for some $\beta > 0$. Downhill steps are thus always accepted, but uphill steps are accepted with a probability which decreases with the size of the uphill step. It is this feature of sometimes accepting adverse moves that distinguishes simulated annealing from standard optimisation procedures, such as those of section 3, and allows the algorithm to escape from local extrema.

To convert (9) into an algorithm, several aspects of the procedure require further definition:

1. Step Length. Simulated annealing can be used in the design of experiments either to search a list of candidate points, or to search over a continuous design region χ. In the former case the points x_k and x_l for exchange might be selected at random. In the second case x_l would be a distance Δr from x_0 in a random direction.

2. Cooling. Simulated annealing was originally suggested by analogy with the annealing of metals by slow cooling. This suggests taking $\beta = 1/kT$, where the 'temperature' T is slowly reduced during the optimisation run, in order to decrease the probability of accepting detrimental steps in (9). The analogy does not, however, suggest the rate at which T should be reduced. Suppose, instead, that the value of the function at the minimum, ϕ_{min}, were known, although its location x_{min} was unknown and was to be found. Then replacement of the second condition of (9) by

$$p = \exp \{-\beta \Delta \phi / (\phi - \phi_{min})\} \tag{10}$$

yields a probability of accepting detrimental steps which decreases as the global minimum is approached. Usually ϕ_{min} will not be known, but it can be replaced by an estimate, which can be revised in the light of computational experience. When finding an exact D-optimum design, a first guess at this limit might be 90% of the value for the continuous design.

3. Probability of Acceptance. It remains to determine β, which should be chosen so that sufficient detrimental steps are taken to allow the algorithm to escape from any local minima. This suggests that, for each run of the algorithm, the probability of accepting uphill steps should lie between 0.5 and 0.9.

4. Stopping Rule. The algorithm can be terminated when a specified number of successive trials, between perhaps 20 and 50, fail to produce an accepted step.

A major disadvantage of some applications of simulated annealing is that the performance of the method can depend critically on parameters, such as the rate of cooling, which are hard to determine. However, the two parameters, β and ϕ_{min}, required by the steps given above, can readily be found from a few numerical experiments.

Example 3. Concentration of a neurone transmitter
The model

$$E(Y_i) = \theta_1[\exp(-\theta_3 t_{i-1}) - \exp(-\theta_3 t_i)] + \theta_2(t_i - t_{i-1}) \tag{11}$$

was used by Bates (1983) to model the concentration of a neurotransmitter in solution as a function of the time of immersion of a brain slice: t_i is the time when the slice is moved from vial i to vial i+1 and $t_0 = 0$. There were 11 vials so that N = 11. The total time for the experiment was 30 minutes, leading to the constraint $t_{11} \leq 30$. The feature that makes this an interesting numerical problem in the design of experiments is the constraint on the minimum time that the tissue can be in a vial. In Bates's formulation this was one minute, so that $t_i - t_{i-1} \geq 1$. Bohachevsky et al. generalise this to obtain a series of designs for a variety of minimum times.

The model (11) contains one nonlinear parameter. This was set at a single prior value, 0.25, and the model linearised about this point. For the linearised model F is an 11×3 matrix for which the locally D-optimum design was found using simulated annealing to minimise $-|F^T F|$, or equivalently to maximise $|F^T F|$. The initial estimate of the maximum of $|F^T F|$ was 71, the value found by Bates using conventional optimisation methods. This value was too low and was increased in approximately 1% steps, the optimum design yielding a value of 105.3. The values of β varied between 10 and 100, clustering near 75, although the actual value was not found to be critical.

The search for the optimum design is made relatively fast by use of the generalisation of (6) to evaluate potential steps – the design need only be updated if a step is accepted. The algorithm uses a random direction to define each step. If the proposed step violates any constraints it can be rejected before the design function is evaluated.

5 RELATED WORK, FURTHER READING

The emphasis in this paper has been on D-optimality in which the generalised variance of the parameter estimates is minimised. The General Equivalence Theorem states that D-optimum continuous designs ξ^* are also G-optimum. That is, if the information matrix of a design is $M(\xi)$, the variance of the predicted response at x, standardised for N and σ^2, is

$$d(x,\xi) = f^T(x) \, M^{-1}(\xi) \, f(x)$$

Then if

$$\bar{d}(\xi) = \max_{x \in \chi} d(x,\xi) \tag{12}$$

the G-optimum continuous design minimises $\bar{d}(\xi)$, with $\bar{d}(\xi^*) = p$ at the points of the optimum design.

Although the equivalence of D- and G-optimum designs must hold for continuous designs, it does not necessarily do so for exact designs, which have to be separately calculated. A related criterion is V-optimality, in which the maximum in (12) is replaced by minimising the average variance over a region which is usually χ.

In principle it is easy to modify the exchange, and other, algorithms for criteria other than D-optimality. For example Welch (1984) describes how DETMAX (Mitchell, 1974) can be adapted to generate G- and V-optimum designs. In the application of simulated annealing reported by Haines (1987), D-, G- and V-optimum exact designs were found for a variety of polynomial models. The search was over a continuous design region, rather than over the list of candidate points of the algorithms of section 3. Her comparisons with the K-exchange of Cook and Nachtsheim (1980) indicate that the exchange algorithm is preferable for D-optimality, the annealing algorithm for G-optimality, but that there is little to choose between the algorithms for V-optimality.

Algorithms of the exchange type and simulated annealing are the two most widely studied methods of constructing D-optimum designs. Meyer and Nachtsheim (1988) show that simulated annealing is appreciably better suited to searching over lists of candidate points than to searching over continuous design regions. Atkinson (1992) investigates generalised simulated annealing when there is a limit on the number of function evaluations. His study of a D-optimum design problem over a non-standard design region leads to the development of a segmented simulated annealing procedure.

Simulated annealing is not the only heuristic algorithm which might be suitable for design problems. Woodruff and Rocke (1992) compare simulated annealing, genetic algorithms and tabu search for a combinatorial optimisation problem resulting from the robust estimation of minimum volume ellipsoids. Another general method of search is that of branch and bound, which is applied by Welch (1982) to finding globally D-optimum designs over a list of candidate points. The method guarantees to find the optimum design. However, the computational requirements increase rapidly with the size of the problem.

REFERENCES

Atkinson, A. C. (1992) A simulation analysis of simulated annealing. Technical report, Department of Statistical and Mathematical Sciences, London School of Economics.

Atkinson, A. C. and Donev, A. N. (1989) The construction of exact D-optimum experimental designs with application to blocking response surface designs. Biometrika 76: 515–526.

Atkinson, A. C. and Donev, A. N. (1992) Optimum Experimental Designs. Oxford: Clarendon Press.

Bates, D. (1983) The derivative of $|X^TX|$ and its uses. Technometrics 25: 373-376.

Bohachevsky, I. O., Johnson, M. E. and Stein, M. L. (1986) Generalized simulated annealing for function optimization. Technometrics 28: 209-217.

Box, M. J. and Draper, N. R. (1971) Factorial designs, the $|X'X|$ criterion, and some related matters. Technometrics 13: 731–742.

Cook, R. D. and Nachtsheim, C. J. (1980) A comparison of algorithms for constructing exact D-optimal designs. Technometrics 22: 315–324.

Cook, R. D. and Nachtsheim, C. J. (1989) Computer-aided blocking of factorial and response surface designs. Technometrics 31: 339–346.

Donev, A. N. (1988) The construction of exact D-optimum experimental designs. University of London PhD thesis.

Fedorov, V. V. (1972) Theory of Optimal Experiments. New York: Academic Press.

Galil, Z. and Kiefer, J. (1980) Time- and space-saving computer methods, related to Mitchell's DETMAX, for finding D-optimum designs. Technometrics 22: 301–313.

Haines, L. M. (1987) The application of the annealing algorithm to the construction of exact optimal designs for linear-regression models. Technometrics 29: 439–447.

Kiefer, J. and Wolfowitz, J. (1960) The equivalence of two extrema problems. Can. J. Math. 12: 363–366.

Kurotschka, V. G. (1981) A general approach to optimum design of experiments with qualitative and quantitative factors. In 'Statistics: Applications and New Directions: proceedings of the Indian Statistical Institute Golden Jubilee International Conference, 1981' (eds. J. K. Ghosh and J. Roy), pp. 353–368. Calcutta: Indian Statistical Institute.

Meyer, R. K. and Nachtsheim, C. J. (1988) Constructing exact D-optimal experimental designs by simulated annealing. Amer. J. Math. and Man. Sci. 8, 329–359.

Mitchell, T. J. (1974) An algorithm for the construction of 'D-optimal' experimental designs. Technometrics 16: 203–210.

Rao, C. R. (1965) Linear Statistical Inference and its Applications. New York: Wiley.

Welch, W. J. (1982) Branch-and-bound search for experimental designs based on D-optimality and other criteria. Technometrics 24: 41–48.

Welch, W. J. (1984) Computer-aided design of experiments for response estimation. Technometrics 26: 217–224.

Woodruff, D. L. and Rocke, D. M. (1992) Computation of minimum volume ellipsoid estimates using heuristic search. Technical report, Graduate School of Management, University of California, Davis.

9 FRIL: a support logic programming system

J. F. Baldwin*, T. P. Martin and B. W. Pilsworth
FRIL Systems Limited, Bristol ITeC
Advanced Computing Research Centre, Faculty of Engineering,
University of Bristol

1 INTRODUCTION

1.1 Uncertainty in Rule-based Systems

FRIL is a generalisation of logic programming which, in addition to the purely deductive reasoning process of Prolog, allows for inference under uncertainty in the face of incompleteness of evidence and vague, natural language descriptions of knowledge. The motivation for this extension of logic programming is the recognition of the pervasiveness of uncertainty in all realistic practical applications. There is no guarantee of truth in the knowledge which people have, and so there is a need to model both fuzzy and probabilistic imprecision when representing and reasoning about their expertise.

Commonsense reasoning takes into account frequent conjunctions of propositions rather than constant conjunctions, probabilistic causality rather than deterministic causality, a rationality based on "may be" rather than "will" and which cannot be guaranteed always to be right. An expert system uses facts and rules in a knowledge base to capture the expertise of a human expert. Given that this is possible, many of the rules used will correspond to "rules of thumb" which people are so good at acquiring and using. These rules of thumb may come about as a summary of many more precise rules. It is a characteristic of human reasoning that complexity is often controlled by summarising knowledge; and although this generally introduces imprecision, it can also engender a quality of robustness in the reasoning process. This robustness is further enhanced by the feedback provided by people's propensity to check conclusions from different points of view which focuses the inference process. Moreover, human reasoning is efficient by avoiding the exploration of unlikely

---

* Professor Baldwin is SERC Senior Research Fellow.

alternatives, and it is risk-taking by appropriate simplification so that long chains of argument are avoided.

The incompleteness of information in practical knowledge engineering systems means that the deductive style of reasoning of classical logic must be enhanced by inductive, abductive and plausible reasoning styles of inference. Analogical reasoning is also important and all of these different modes of inference require mechanisms for handling uncertainty. Reasoning by means of cues, where a context is suggestive of particular sources of evidence, is another example of uncertain inference. One particular body of evidence may be supportive of a statement, whilst another may support its negation. The different evidences must be compared and combined to give a final judgement on whether the statement is to be accepted or rejected, and the lack of sufficient information means that the commitment, for or against, involves a risk. When assessing a candidate for employment in a firm one must weigh up the evidence on the basis of criteria such as qualifications, motivation, independence, cooperativeness, flexibility, leadership and so on. If a particular individual is very highly qualified, but does not get on well with people, he or she may not be suitable for working in a team.

It is said that a rational person makes proper use of reason and this implies, amongst other things, that he or she correctly estimates the strength of available evidence and the degrees of support for propositions based on this evidence. In the most favourable cases the premises of an argument entail its conclusion, so that if the premises are true then the conclusion must also be true. This has limited application in practice because of the various forms of uncertainty that are inevitably present, and in general evidence will not logically support a conclusion in this sense. On the other hand, the evidence may not support the negation of the conclusion either, so that all that can be deduced is that the truth of the conclusion is uncertain. In general the evidence may give preferential support for a conclusion in comparison with its negation, and it is necessary to deduce degrees of support for a given statement and the negation of that statement. For example, in the context of a criminal law trial, it is necessary for the jury to weigh the evidence for and against the defendant. The evidence may be in partial conflict, it may include information of questionable reliability and descriptions may be vague, ambiguous or imprecise in some way. Pure probabilistic reasoning is not sufficient to model all these contexts because it is founded on the very precise framework of classical set theory, and a complement law for negation which is at odds with the above interpretation of evidence for and against a proposition. For this reason, a more general model of uncertain reasoning is required.

1.2   Probabilistic and Fuzzy Uncertainties

In general, incomplete information can be of two types: one concerns a lack of specific or relevant data, and the other concerns a lack of concept definition. For example, in a vision understanding system, only part of an object may be in view because a building may be occluding it. This gives rise to probabilistic uncertainty concerning what the object might be because the visible part could belong to several different artefacts. If occlusion was removed so that the whole object was in view, then it might be possible to identify it for certain. On the other hand the description which most naturally identifies it might itself give doubt as to the precise nature of the object. For example, the description "a large saloon car" is suggestive of an instance of a class of objects which is sufficiently informative for most purposes. But it lacks precise detail on the meaning of the terms "large", "saloon" and even "car", so that some doubt as to the nature of the object remains. This type of fuzzy uncertainty is characteristic of people's efficient and robust method of communication and understanding of concepts by natural language descriptions.

Heuristic knowledge often combines both probabilistic and fuzzy types of uncertainty. For example the statement "bright students do well in exams" is a rule of thumb which might be better expressed as: "if a student is bright then he or she will probably do well in exams". The inclusion of the qualifier "probably" shows that the rule cannot be guaranteed to be true, but it is nevertheless true for most bright students. An expert who suggested this rule for inclusion in the knowledge base of an expert system, might then be asked to be more precise on the meaning of the word "probably". One natural interpretation would be as follows: "the probability that a person, selected at random from a population of students, would do well in exams given that he or she was bright, is high"; and this is suggestive of the following vague conditional probability assignment:

$$Pr(\_Student\ does\ well\ in\ exams|\ \_Student\ is\ bright) = high$$

where _Student is a variable corresponding to any person selected at random from the population of students. The replacement of "high" by some single valued probability, such as 0.9, would be somewhat arbitrary and artificial. More realistic would be to characterise the uncertainty by a probability interval such as [0.8, 0.95] which expresses some doubt as to the precise probability assignment and which provides a powerful and flexible way of incorporating a sensitivity analysis into the reasoning process. A further refinement might be to use a fuzzy set characterisation for "high", but this can lead to an unnecessarily large computational burden when the probability interval often provides a sufficient representation for the inherent uncertainty in the heuristic rule. Fuzzy sets can be very useful, however, in representing the meaning of semantic terms such as "does well in exams". The concept could be defined on a domain [0, 100] of average percentage scores such that any score above 70 satisfies the concept exactly and any scores below 50 does not satisfy the concept at all. A FRIL program fragment which models this heuristic knowledge is as follows:

(good_score [50:0, 70:1])

((exam_result _Student good_score) (bright _Student)) : (0.8 0.95)

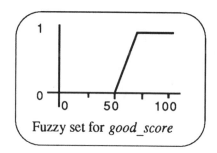

Fuzzy set for *good_score*

The combination in FRIL of representing conditional probability values by support pairs and semantic terms by means of fuzzy sets imposes a very modest computational burden, given the very expressive notation, and it includes the significant advantage of a built-in sensitivity analysis for interpreting the impact of uncertain inferences. In fact, FRIL characterises the probability interval by means of a support pair, and this is the fundamental form of representation of uncertainty in the support logic programming paradigm. The matching of semantic terms defined as fuzzy sets also has a natural probabilistic interpretation, so that the degree of match can also be derived as a support pair inference.

Expert systems such as MYCIN manipulate certainty factors to provide weights of evidence. These and other methods, such as the adapted Bayesian inference scheme of PROSPECTOR, are often ad hoc to a large degree, but nevertheless seem to work in practice in restricted applications. This emphasises the importance of having an inference mechanism which models uncertainty. The support logic programming paradigm of FRIL provides a more formal approach to uncertain inference which includes probabilistic reasoning and semantic matching of fuzzy concepts as special cases.

1.3   Extension of Logic Programming Framework

The representation of facts and rules of a FRIL support logic knowledge base is a simple notational extension of the Horn clause logic representation of the logic programming paradigm of Prolog – probabilities, support pairs or lists of support pairs are annexed to the clauses to represent the conditional supports. A list-based syntax is adopted for both Prolog and support logic clauses, which contrasts with the functor notation of the more traditional Edinburgh syntax Prologs.

The support logic reasoning mechanism also contrasts significantly with the depth-first inference strategy of Prolog. Support logic inference involves combining support from different proof paths as well as accumulating the support along particular proof paths; and this entails a mixture of depth and breadth search inference strategies. For this reason it is inappropriate to implement the support logic inference mechanism in Prolog, although such a simulation has been done as a feasibility study, and this demonstrated that the computational overhead was unacceptably high. The implementation of support logic programming as part of the core system means that applications of significant complexity involving heuristic knowledge can realistically be implemented in FRIL. The breadth inference mechanism also embodies a considerable degree of natural concurrency which could in principle be exploited by parallel hardware although this has not yet been done.

By contrast with the usual interpretation of programs in conventional procedural languages, viz.

$$\text{algorithm} + \text{data} = \text{program}$$

the declarative style of Prolog programming has,

$$\text{logic} + \text{control} = \text{logic program}$$

whereas FRIL has in addition to this,

$$\text{probability} + \text{logic} + \text{control} = \text{support logic program.}$$

Furthermore, the support logic inference mechanism of FRIL more closely approximates the ideal of a true logic programming language than Prolog, by incorporating an 'open world' semantics model and true logic negation instead of the 'closed world' model of Prolog which only has 'negation by failure'.

2   A PROLOG PROGRAMMING ENVIRONMENT

The language FRIL embodies all the features of Prolog which has established itself as a powerful programming environment for the representation of certain restricted kinds of relational knowledge. Prolog has also proved itself as a versatile systems programming language for the construction of expert system shells, man-machine interfaces and similar applications in artificial intelligence. Some advantages of the Prolog style of programming are as follows:

- It encourages a high-level declarative style of programming such that programs can have a close correspondence to their problem specifications. This facilitates rapid prototyping, simple maintenance and consequent robustness of code.
- It is based on the Horn clause subset of predicate logic. This allows simple and efficient implementations of the language to be made so that programs run fast. For example, Prolog programs have performed favourably compared with compiled LISP which is another language widely used in artificial intelligence work.

The FRIL system is implemented in 'C' and includes a complete Prolog language which is designed according to the most up-to-date principles of the Warren Abstract Machine concept for Logic Programming languages [Warren 1983], extended to model the support logic programming capability.

The Prolog language subset of FRIL includes all of the standard features associated with other established Prolog systems plus some extensions – for example: recursive programming style and list processing; the standard depth-first search inference strategy with backtracking; control of backtracking using cut; systems and meta-programming activities such as: database manipulation facilities, procedural programming and control, debugging tools, expert system shells, and high-level knowledge representation using conceptual graphs. The simple example of the "append" predicate, defined below, illustrates the recursive list processing style:

```
((append () _List _List))
((append (_Head|_Tail) _List (_Head|_Rest) )
      (append _Tail _List _Rest))
```

3   SUPPORT LOGIC PROGRAMMING

3.1   Support Pairs

The basic unit of measurement of uncertainty in FRIL is the support pair which defines an interval as a subset of [0, 1] in which the unknown probability lies. The need for support pairs in rule-based systems, as opposed to single valued probability measures, is very simply illustrated by an example which generalises the modus ponens form of argument in classical logic. By modus ponens, with P ⊂ Q, and P is true, we can deduce Q is true. However, suppose P ⊂ Q as before, but the probability of P is x, i.e. Pr(P) = x; then all that can be deduced about Q is that Pr(Q) lies in the interval [x, 1] which is modelled in FRIL by the support pair (x 1). The lower limit of the support pair is called the necessary support, and the upper limit is called the possible support. It should be emphasised that the limits are not themselves measures of probability, they simply prescribe the interval which contains the unknown probability value. If nothing at all was known about a particular fact, then the appropriate support pair would be (0 1) indicating that the probability of the fact being true lies between 0 and 1, representing total uncertainty. On the other hand the support pair (1 1) represents true for sure or probability 1, and (0 0) represents false for sure or probability 0.

The distinction between (0 1) and (0 0) is particularly interesting in the context of logic programming. Prolog operates under the assumption of a closed world database, so that only those relations which appear explicitly in the database are taken to be true. Falsity is then interpreted as failure to prove a goal true with respect to that database, so that the negation of a goal succeeds if the goal fails to be proved. This means that if a particular relation is not present in the database, then it will be taken to be false. On the other hand support logic programming makes a clear distinction between falsity represented by the support pair (0 0) and total uncertainty represented by (0 1). In this case, if a particular relation is not present in the knowledge base, or is otherwise totally uncertain, then it will be inferred with (0 1) support; but any definitely false relations will be inferred with (0 0) support through the support logic inference process. Thus support logic programming embodies open world semantics, and a complement rule for negation ensures that the negation of true (1 1) is false (0 0) and vice-versa. Furthermore, the negation of total uncertainty (0 1) is also (0 1).

Consider the following example:

((academically_stronger Mary Bill)) : (0.7 0.9)

This statement associates a probability between 0.7 and 0.9 with the proposition: "Mary is academically stronger than Bill". This probability interval could have been established by a comparison of their past academic achievements, for example. The necessary support for the proposition is 0.7 and the possible support is 0.9. Moreover, the necessary support against the proposition is 1 − 0.9 = 0.1, and the possible support against the proposition is 1 − 0.7 = 0.3. This means that the support pair for the negation of the statement is (0.1 0.3). More generally, the following relationships always hold:

Necessary support for a proposition

+ Necessary support against the proposition ≤ 1

Necessary support for proposition

= 1 − Possible support against proposition

Necessary support against proposition

= 1 − Possible support for proposition

Possible support for proposition

= 1 − Necessary support against proposition

Possible support against proposition

= 1 − Necessary support for proposition

A useful interpretation of the support pair is that it can represent a pattern of voting behaviour for a population sample. The necessary support represents the proportion of the population voting in favour of the proposition and the complement of the possible support (i.e. 1 − possible support) represents the proportion voting against. The difference, possible support − necessary support, represents the proportion who abstain.

3.2   Inference Philosophy

Having defined the support pair as the basic unit of uncertainty measurement, it is necessary to define a calculus for combining support pairs appropriately, given a knowledge base comprised of a set of compound statements made up of propositions joined together with logic operators. Rules defined as clauses with conditional supports provide the principal method of representation of such compound statements. A rule clause in FRIL comprises a list of "atoms" with the first element defining the 'head' of the clause, and the tail of the list comprising the 'body', which list of atoms is interpreted as a conjunction of goals. Consider, for example the following extension of the rule introduced in section 1.2 above:

((exam_result _Student good_score) (bright _Student)) : ((0.8 0.95) (0.1 0.2))

In this case there are two support pairs (expressing probability intervals) associated with the rule which have the following conditional probability interpretation:

Pr(_Student's exam result is a good score | _Student is bright)

is in [0.8, 0.95]

Pr(_Student's exam result is a good score | it is

false that _Student is bright) is in [0.1, 0.2]

Suppose that it is known that for a particular student John, Pr(John is bright) is in [0.8, 1]. Then the probability that John's exam result will be a good score can be calculated by a computation law which is based on the following theorem of total probability:

Pr(head) = Pr(head | body).Pr(body) + Pr(head | notbody).Pr(notbody)

This computation law, which derives a support pair inference for 'head', is the fundamental inference rule for support logic programming in FRIL. The only adaptation of the theorem of total probability which is required, is to compute upper and lower bounds on Pr(head) on the basis of support pair characterisations of the probabilities on the right-hand side of the expression. In the case of supports defined as single valued probabilities, the computation law is exactly the above theorem of total probability and so the computation law provides a very natural generalisation of probabilistic reasoning. The FRIL syntax allows the association of a single support pair with a rule and this defines Pr(head | body), and the support pair for Pr(head | notbody) defaults to (0 1).

This law together with laws for support logic conjunction, disjunction and negation define a calculus for support logic inference along a particular proof path, and the computed support for a particular instantiated goal corresponds to one perspective of the contribution of support to the goal. Often this computed support will correspond to support derived from a single clause of the goal predicate. In the case of a predicate with multiple clauses, there may be several ways in which to derive different supports for the particular instantiated goal. These do not represent choices for support but rather contributions to the overall support from the various different perspectives, and it is essential that the inference mechanism always computes all possible solutions so that these can be combined. A second calculus defines how the supports are to be combined, and FRIL offers two choices: an intersection law discussed in section 3.5 and the Dempster combination law discussed in section 3.6, below.

The inference philosophy of support logic programming is based on the principle of deriving sound probabilistic inferences expressed as support pairs on the basis of a set of mutually compatible conditional probability constraints on facts and rules expressed as support clauses. The Dempster combination law is exceptional in that it is used to model the situation of partially conflicting heuristic rules. Apart from this the inferences derived are wholly compatible with probability theory. No distinction is made between the specific evidence supplied by fully instantiated facts, and the general information supplied by heuristic rules; nor is there any explicit characterisation of a priori information, so that the use of Bayes' theorem is not directly applicable to the inference process. Bayes' theorem could be employed as a method of updating the knowledge base on the basis of computed inferences, if required, by using an appropriate FRIL Prolog program.

3.3   The Support Logic Calculus

The complete computation law for the probability inference rule is given below:

$$\begin{array}{l} \text{head "if" body} : ((a\ b)\ (c\ d)) \\ \underline{\text{body} : (x\ y)} \\ \text{therefore, head} : (n\ p) \end{array}$$

where, $n = a.y + c.(1 - y),$ if $a \leq c$

or, $n = a.x + c.(1 - x),$ if $a > c$

and, $p = b.x + d.(1 - x),$ if $b \leq d$

or, $p = b.y + d.(1 - y),$ if $b > d$

In the case that the rule has a single support pair associated with it, say (a b), so that (c d) = (0 1), then the inference rule simplifies to the following:

$$n = a.x, \qquad\qquad p = b.x + 1 - x$$

The law for support logic negation is obvious given the interpretation of necessary and possible supports described in section 3.1 above, and it is defined by the following complement rule:

$$\begin{array}{l} \underline{\text{goal} : (a\ b)} \\ \text{"not" goal} : (n\ p), \end{array}$$

where, $n = 1 - b;$ and, $p = 1 - a$

The choices of conjunction law (and also disjunction) are discussed in section 3.4 below. The combination laws for multiple sources of evidence are discussed in sections 3.5 and 3.6 following.

3.4 Conjunction Laws

Since probability logic is non-truth functional, it is not possible to determine a point value probability for the conjunction of two propositions given probability assignments on each proposition alone, unless some assumption is made such as the degree of mutual dependence between the two propositions. However, since the probabilities of the two propositions are characterised by support pairs, it is possible to obtain a probability interval constraint on the probability of the conjunction of the two propositions, thus:

> proposition1 : (a b)
> proposition2 : (c d)
> proposition1 "and" proposition2 : $(0 \vee (a + c - 1) \quad b \wedge d)$

where $\vee$ denotes the maximum, and $\wedge$ denotes the minimum operator. Note that for any choices of α in (a b) and β in (c d), the product a.b is contained in the required interval $[0 \vee (a+c-1), b \wedge d]$, and this choice for the conjunction corresponds to independence between the propositions. The upper limit, $b \wedge d$, corresponds to an assumption of strict implication between the propositions, that is to say either proposition1 strictly implies proposition2 or viceversa, and this assumption has a useful application for the interpretation of conjunction with fuzzy sets. On the other hand the lower limit for conjunction, $0 \vee (a+c-1)$, corresponds to the maximum possible mutual exclusiveness between the propositions consistent with the probability values.

In FRIL the assumption of independence is taken as the default, as the corresponding multiplicative conjunction law is consistent with the maximum entropy principle of minimum prejudice given no additional constraints:

> proposition1 : (a b)
> proposition2 : (c d)
> proposition1 "and" proposition2 : (a.c b.d).

In practice, the selection of support for conjunction as the whole interval $[0 \vee (a+c-1), b \wedge d]$ generally appears too extreme a choice, as uncertainty will often propagate very rapidly through the inference process and support pairs approach (0 1), so that total uncertainty is all that can be inferred. However, the law is sometimes useful and a FRIL built-in predicate "conj" is provided to model it. The following examples illustrate the different forms of conjunction – the symbol "qs", used below, denotes a FRIL built-in predicate for support logic query evaluation:

$$((a\ obj)) : (0.7\ 0.8)$$
$$((b\ obj)) : (0.9\ 1)$$
$$((c\ obj)) : (0.8\ 0.9)$$

query,   qs ((a _Object) (b _Object) (c _Object))   % default law applies
obtains,   ((a obj) (b obj) (c obj)) : (0.504 0.72)
query,   qs ((conj (a _Object) (b _Object) (c _Object))) % "conj" law used
obtains,   ((conj (a obj) (b obj) (c obj))) : (0.4 0.8)

Note that the default multiplicative conjunction law applies whenever the context is a simple catenation of atoms, whether this be in the body of a rule, or a conjunction of goals as above.

3.5   Intersection Combination Law

The default law for combining supports from different proof paths is that the probability intervals which the support pairs define are intersected together. More specifically:

proposition : (a b)   % from path 1
proposition : (c d)   % from path 2
infer proposition : (n p)

where,   n = a∨c,   and,   p = b∧d;

provided that the constraints, $a \le d$ and $c \le b$ are satisfied. If these constraints are not satisfied, then the probability intervals do not overlap, there is no solution and FRIL will generate an error message.

The rationale for this law is that it is assumed that the rules of FRIL are used to provide alternative ways of proving a conclusion such that the intervals associated with the support pairs for the various proof paths are consistent. Therefore, a point in the interval associated with the support pair for the combined proof must also be in each of the intervals of the individual proofs. Hence the final interval is obtained by intersecting the intervals corresponding to the various proof paths.

Care must be taken to ensure that the support logic clauses which define the different proof paths satisfy mutual constraints of compatibility and consistency. Satisfaction of these constraints is not always easy to prove which is a reflection of the difficulties that one can encounter in inductive reasoning in comparison with the more straightforward deductive inference. However, when a knowledge base is appropriately modelled, the intersection law provides a very powerful way of incorporating feedback in the inference process when combining supports from multiple sources of evidence. If all probabilities were expressed simply as point values, then every proof path for a particular goal would have to derive exactly the same probability inference to satisfy the constraint of global consistency of the knowledge base. Such redundancy would be quite sterile, and there could be no value in it. However, the incompleteness of information introduces probability intervals via support pairs, and the combination of such uncertainty with the redundancy inherent in multiple proof paths derives a focusing of the reasoning process and an invaluable increase in the precision of the inference through feedback.

3.6   Dempster Combination Law

If a support logic predicate is declared to be of type 'Dempster' prior to its definition, then multiple support clauses which define this predicate are assumed to correspond to independent viewpoints, and these will have the potential for partial conflict in the inferences derived from such viewpoints. Independence in this context means that the different viewpoints have no prior connection nor any influence upon one another. The rationale for the Dempster combination law is that there always exists some conflict between such multiple sources of evidence, and an estimation of such conflict is made on the basis of an initial assignment of support for the joint occurrence of the different sources of evidence. The support corresponding to the estimated conflict is redistributed by a process of normalisation, regardless of whether there is any foundation for the presumption of such conflict. The law is ad hoc and does not have the probabilistic semantics of the remainder of the support logic calculus. However, the case of partial conflict is very difficult to treat using purely probabilistic methods and the Dempster law provides a useful way of treating multiple independent evidence when conflict is expected.

The Dempster combination law is defined as follows:

Dempster pred

proposition : (a b)

% 1st inferred proposition expressed in terms of "pred"

proposition : (c d)

% 2nd inferred proposition expressed in terms of "pred"

infer proposition : (n p)

where, $n = (a + c - a.c - k)/(1 - k)$

and, $p = b.d/(1 - k)$

where,   conflict, $k = a.(1 - d) + c.(1 - b)$

4   FUZZY SETS AND SEMANTIC UNIFICATION

4.1   Representation of Fuzzy Sets

A fuzzy set is a generalisation of the classical "crisp" set, to allow for borderline cases where elements are neither wholly included nor wholly excluded by the fuzzy set definition. Fuzzy sets are defined by means of their membership functions which are generalisations of the characteristic functions of ordinary sets. A characteristic function, c, is a mapping from some domain or universe of discourse, D, onto the pair {0, 1}. The membership function, m, generalises this to a mapping from D onto the real valued interval [0, 1], of membership values. A fuzzy set on a real valued domain of discourse, with continuous membership function, is approximated in FRIL by means of an "itype" definition. This represents the continuous curve of the membership function by continuous piece-wise linear segments. For example, the following itype definition is a model of the fuzzy concept of approximately equal to 3:

(about3 [2:0, 3:1, 4:0])

The degree of membership: for values v less than or equal to 2 is zero; for values v greater than 4 is zero; for values v between 2 and 3 is given by the increasing ramp function v-2; and for values v between 3 and 4 is given by the decreasing ramp function 4-v. Memberships for domain values other than the given 2, 3 and 4 are computed by linear interpolation – hence the name "itype". For example, the domain value 2.5 has membership 0.5. There are currently two principal usages of the fuzzy set representation in FRIL applications. One is to do arithmetic with fuzzy number definitions, and the other is to perform a semantic match between terms defined as itype definitions, by a process called semantic unification.

4.2   Fuzzy Arithmetic

FRIL allows basic arithmetic operations on fuzzy numbers (i.e. fuzzy sets on a real valued domain). The built-in arithmetic predicates "sum" for addition and subtraction, and "times" for multiplication and division, provide for the arithmetic processing of fuzzy numbers with certain restrictions and approximations. A pair of fuzzy numbers can be added, subtracted, multiplied and divided. Division in which the divisor is a fuzzy set with non-zero membership for domain value 0, generates a division by zero error message as expected. The computed products and divisions of fuzzy numbers are piece-wise linear segment approximations to the correct fuzzy number representations.

4.3   Semantic Unification

The FRIL support logic mechanism extends the purely syntactic unification of FRIL Prolog by computing the degree of support for the match between semantic terms defined as fuzzy sets (itypes). For example, suppose that the fact ((interview_score John about3)) is defined in the knowledge base where about3 is the fuzzy set defined in section 4.1 above; and suppose it is required to compute the support for the goal (interview_score John above_average), where above_average is defined by the following fuzzy set:

$$(above\_average \ [2:0, \ 4:1])$$

There is a degree of match between the semantic terms "about3" and "above_average" and this is computed according to the following interpretation of semantic match. It is desired to compute the conditional support for John is "above_average" given that it is known that John is "about3". In other words it is required to compute support for ("above_average" | "about3"). The fuzzy set "about3" induces a constraint or restriction on a family of probability densities F, of which r, say, is a typical member. The probability of "above_average" given F is then defined as the expected value of the membership function, m, for "above_average" as follows:

$$Pr("above\_average" \ | \ "about3") = \int \mu \rho$$

Since ρ is only a typical density from the family, F, of such densities, the integral defines a range of probability values. The corresponding support pair for the conditional match is then obtained by minimising and maximising the integral with respect to $\rho \in F$. This computation is most effectively performed by using a discrete fuzzy set approximate model.

5   APPLICATIONS OF FRIL

5.1   Types and Areas of Application

The support logic programming paradigm of FRIL is suitable for modelling a very broad range of applications in artificial intelligence in general, with particular emphasis on knowledge engineering or expert systems. These include: planning systems, robotics, short-term weather forecasting, stock market and financial planning, weighing the evidence in legal cases, intelligent CAD and CAM, intelligent tutoring systems, medical applications and cognitive science research. More specifically, some applications which have been explored by industry using FRIL, with involvement by either FRIL Systems Limited or the

Advanced Computing Research Centre of the University of Bristol are the following:

- Pattern recognition using neural nets
- Musical composition and sound synthesis
- Handwritten script recognition
- Development of expert system tools
- Software dependability modelling – for management of software life cycle
- Quantifying uncertainty in software cost estimation
- Control of radiation waste
- Analogical reasoning and machine learning
- Measurement of software diversity – for fault tolerant software

- Natural language understanding systems

    Conceptual graphs have been used for high-level representation of contextual and semantic knowledge, and fuzzy sets have been used to express qualifiers and meanings of linguistic terms. This model has been used as an intelligent front end to a database, and includes the capability to handle elliptical and anaphoric reference.

- Command and control projects

    Neural nets are being used for "perception" by signal detection, and support logic reasoning provides a model for semantic interpretation of the neural net outputs.

- Fuzzy control

    A real-time linguistic fuzzy controller has been developed using support logic programming which is a more flexible alternative to the conventional fuzzy control model. The new model retains the support logic representation of heuristic rules with fuzzy set representation of terms, and it has been successfully applied to achieve robust real-time control of problems like "the inverted pendulum" [Yamakawa, 1989] and variations on this problem, like the open-loop unstable pivoted beam.

- Probabilistic scene analysis and vision understanding

    Conceptual graph schemas have been used to represent background and contextual knowledge, and conceptual graphs with fuzzy set representations and support logic reasoning have been used for hypothesis generation to guide the search for objects in a static two-dimensional image of a scene, and aid image interpretation.

- Expert systems design with composite materials

  This application in the aerospace industry has employed heuristic modelling in FRIL interfaced with traditional algorithmic languages for simulation modelling and numerical analysis.

- Client administration expert system – for money market services

  This industrially-based project has used conceptual graphs in FRIL for the development of an expert system for vetting orders and automating quality control.

5.2   An Illustrative Application Example

The following FRIL program fragment is an elementary example of a support logic knowledge base which incorporates many of the modelling features for reasoning under uncertainty which are provided in FRIL.

The knowledge base begins with six fuzzy set definitions:

```
(excellent [3:0, 5:1])
(above_average [2:0, 4:1])
(about3 [2:0, 3:1, 4:0])

(very_high [24:0, 30:1])
(high [20:0, 26:1])
(fairly_high [18:0, 22:1, 26:1, 30:0])
```

The follows the knowledge base of (highly simplified) general information concerning what constitutes a good candidate for entry onto an academic course in a British university, expressed as heuristic support logic rules:

```
((good_candidate  _Student)
        (ucca_profile  _Student suitable)
        (interview_score  _Student above_average)) : ((1 1) (0 0.5))
((good_candidate  _Student)
        (ucca_profile  _Student suitable)) : ((0.7 1) (0 0.1))

((ucca_profile  _Student suitable)
        (predicted_grades  _Student high)
        (school_report  _Student sound)) : ((0.8 1) (0 0.3))
((ucca_profile  _Student suitable)
```

(predicted_grades _Student very_high)) : (0.9 1)

The knowledge base is completed with the following examples of specific information concerning two candidates, John and Mary, for entry onto a course:

((predicted_grades John fairly_high))
((predicted_grades Mary 25))

((school_report John sound)) : (0.6 0.8)
((school_report Mary sound)) : (0.9 1)

((interview_score John about3))
((interview_score Mary excellent))

The following support logic query (using built-in query evaluator "qs") derives the appropriate inferences shown:

qs ((good_candidate X))

((good_candidate John)) : (0.067 0.787)
((good_candidate Mary)) : (0.45 0.895)

The fuzzy set definitions should be reasonably self-explanatory, except to say that "excellent", "above_average" and "about3" are fuzzy sets on the domain [0, 5] of interview score; and "very_high", "high" and "fairly_high" are fuzzy sets on the domain [0, 30] of predicted grades. Furthermore, "excellent", "above_average", "very_high" and "high" have monotonically increasing membership functions representing fuzzifications of the "≥" relation; and "about3" and "fairly_high" are uni-modal membership functions representing approximate ranges.

The knowledge base of heuristic rules comprises two support logic predicates. "good_candidate" comprises two support clauses: the first expresses the knowledge that there is strong support for the candidate being good if the information that he or she has a suitable 'UCCA' profile (from the standard student entry form) and his or her interview score is above average, is true; and there is only weak support against the candidate being good if the same information is false. The second clause expresses a relative importance for the "UCCA profile" in comparison with the interview result, and it states that there is moderate support for the candidate being good if the information that he or she has a suitable 'UCCA' profile is true and there is no information regarding interview result; and there is strong support against the candidate being good if the same information is false. "ucca_profile" also has two support clauses with analogous interpretation to the two clauses for "good_candidate". In particular, "predicted_grades" is treated as being of greater significance than "soundness" of the student from the school report. The single support pair on the second clause is simply shorthand for the information that the support against the student being suitable if it is false that the predicted grades are very high, is totally uncertain (i.e. (0 1) support).

For example, some of the specific data concerning individual students John and Mary is expressed using fuzzy set representations for uncertainty of interview assessment, and expectation of grades (although Mary's predicted grade is given a precise value); whilst the soundness of the students from the school report are assessed by support pair characterisations.

Note that support for Mary being a good candidate is 0.45, whilst the support against is only 0.105. On the other hand, John has more support against being a good candidate than in favour (0.213 support against compared with support 0.067 support for). The inferences are somewhat vague because of the lack of sufficient detail of characterisation of available evidence, but it is nevertheless sufficient to discriminate in favour of Mary as would be expected. The FRIL system incorporates a support logic shell which can be used to explore the uncertainty inference process in more detail.

6 THE FRIL PROGRAMMING ENVIRONMENT

The FRIL programming language comprises a support logic – Prolog combination language which is highly portable due to its implementation in 'C' and available on a wide range of hardware platforms. It is a high performance system due to incremental compilation of clauses, and it includes the following features: modules for systematic development of large scale applications; a foreign language interface for enhancement of the system by user-defined 'C' or Pascal coded routines; on-line help facilities; window environments with scrolling windows, pull-down menus and dialogue boxes – these are being extended to a uniform window interface for all hardware platforms; the facility for the assignment of variable supports for clauses, which can be computed within the clause to reflect context dependence; the representation and processing of discrete fuzzy sets; an applications generator with associated run-time licence arrangements; and a Conceptual Graphs package for high-level knowledge representation.

7 FUTURES DIRECTIONS FOR FRIL

The following are some areas which are currently being researched with a view to their being incorporated in the language FRIL:

- Evidential reasoning tools based on the combining and conditioning of mass assignments;
- A parallel implementation of FRIL;
- Enhancement of fuzzy relational operations;
- Fuzzy controller shell.

REFERENCES

Baldwin, J.F. (1990) Inference under uncertainty for expert systems.

Baldwin, J.F., (1989) Combining Evidences for Evidential Reasoning, University of Bristol internal report, ITRC 150, to appear in the International Journal of Intelligent Systems.

Baldwin, J.F. (1986) Support Logic Programming, in: A.I. Jones et al., Eds., Fuzzy Sets Theory and Applications (Reidel, Dordrecht-Boston).

Baldwin, J.F. (1987) Evidential Support Logic Programming, Fuzzy Sets and Systems, 24, pp. 1–26.

Baldwin, J.F., Martin, T.P. and Pilsworth, B.W. (1988) FRIL Manual, version 4.0, FRIL Systems Ltd, Bristol ITeC, St Anne's House, St Anne's Road, Bristol BS4 4AB, UK.

Baldwin, J.F. (1989) Computational Models of Uncertainty in Expert Systems, Computers & Mathematics with Applications, to appear.

Dempster, A.P. (1968) A generalisation of Bayesian Inference, Journal of Royal Statistical Society, series B, 30.

Warren, D.H.D. (1983) An Abstract Prolog Instruction Set, Technical Note 903, SRI International.

Yamakawa, T. (1989) Stabilization of an inverted pendulum by a high-speed fuzzy logic controller hardware system, Fuzzy Sets and Systems, special issue on applications of fuzzy logic control to industry, Vol. 32, No. 2, pp. 161–180.

Zadeh, L. (1965) Fuzzy sets, Information and Control, 8, pp. 338–353.

10 Computational models of probabilistic reasoning

A. Gammerman
Department of Computer Science, Heriot-Watt University

1   INTRODUCTION

Numerous methods have been suggested and used for dealing with uncertainty in expert systems. Among them: Certainty factor model, Confirmation theory, Endorsements, Possibility theory and others(1). Many of these approaches have been developed in order to overcome particular problems associated with the use of classical formalism for dealing with uncertainty, that is with probability theory. But as it has been pointed out (2) the utility of these theories is still unclear – at least as far as decision making is concerned.

There have been a number of attempts to use the probability theory in expert systems, but most of the implementations followed the so-called Prospector model of uncertainty(3). This uses an inference mechanism based directly on Bayes' rule, but the assumptions implicit in the model are unreasonable. For example, an assumption of independence among different propositions is made which could be hard to justify in practice.

Recent work in statistics has shown that it is possible to adopt sound probabilistic approaches to uncertain inference in expert systems. We consider here two approaches. The first uses Bayesian inference without assuming independence (4) and the second is based on casual graphs, or Bayesian belief networks approach (5, 6).

In this paper we shall describe briefly both models, their design and implementations, and then compare their performance using a medical example.

2   G&T MODEL

In the first model one works through the calculation from first principles, applying Bayes' theorem without assuming independence and estimating joint probability distributions directly from data. There is a widely-held belief that if independence is not assumed, the calculation of probabilities soon becomes unmanageable because of a "combinatorial explosion". However, it was pointed out by Thatcher (7) that it is possible to apply Bayes' theorem without assuming independence and without an unmanageable increase in complexity. Consider for example the problem of estimating the probabilities that patients have certain diseases given their symptoms. If the assumption of independence is dropped, Bayes' theorem leads to a simple, indeed obvious result: if we can identify the past patients who had the same combination of symptoms as a new patient, and look up their final diagnoses, then we can estimate the probabilities for the new patient. We shall call it the "proper Bayes" method in order to distinguish it from the "simple Bayes" method, where the global assumption of independence is made. The reason why the complexity of the proper Bayes approach does not increase exponentially – why there is no "combinatorial explosion" – is that the calculation only involves those propositions and their combinations which actually occur in the database.

With a very large database the method would, in principle, be very simple indeed. However, with a limited database it is necessary to use selected combinations of those symptoms which are most relevant to the diagnosis of each disease. A method is given for selecting such combinations. The method also gives upper and lower confidence limits for each probability, to provide a measure of the precision of the estimates.

A general computational model called G&T has been developed, and it has two major parts; the first is the Selection procedure, and the second is the Matching procedure. The architecture of the system is presented in Figure 1.

In the Selection part the system extracts combinations of relevant symptoms and calculates an estimated probability with corresponding confidence limits for each diagnostic group.

This is summarised in the following **algorithm**:

FOR each of the concerned class i DO

      Calculate 'chi-squared' values for each possible attribute

      IF all objects belongs to the class i

            OR all objects have the same attributes

            OR the highest 'chi-squared' value is lower than a threshold

      THEN

            This combination is terminated with an estimated probability
            of the combination belonging to class i.

      ELSE

            1. Work out the most important attribute among the remaining
               for class i according to the 'chi-squared' values.

            2. Partition the current set of training objects into two subsets
               of including and excluding the selected attribute.

3. Repeat the whole algorithm for each subset until the termination condition is met.

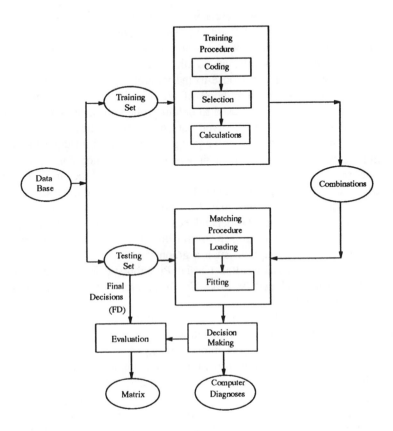

Figure 1 The architecture of the G&T model.

The job of the Matching part is to fit the observed symptoms of newly arrived patients into the combinations of relevant symptoms, and also to find their probabilities.

The G&T system allows decisions to be made for each new patient by selecting the diagnostic group with the highest probability selected (we shall call it the Computer Diagnosis). And the system also allows us to evaluate the accuracy of diagnosis by comparing the computer diagnosis with the patient's final diagnosis recorded by doctors.

3   CASUAL PROBABILISTIC REASONING SYSTEM – CPRS MODEL

The key idea behind the casual models or belief networks' approach is to use either available data or an expert's knowledge to construct the directed acyclic graph (DAG) and then make inferences by exploiting the low-order marginal and conditional probabilities defined over small groups of variables.

A belief network consists of nodes and directed arcs, where each node of the graph represents a variable, and a directed arc between nodes A and B means that knowledge of a response to the variables corresponding to node A may be used to adjust the likelihood of the variables associated with node B. The casual structure may be used to obtain probability assessments between related variables based on either given data or on an expert's opinion. In this state, the graph is unsuitable for propagating evidence, so a different undirected form must subsequently be derived in which new evidence corresponding to any node may be propagated in either direction along the arcs. The new representation of the graph is triangulated into localised groups of variables known as cliques. Probabilities may be stored in terms of these sub-graphs using the information about the dependencies between the variables explicitly stored in the original casual representation. Efficient methods exist for propagating evidence throughout such a graph (5, 8).

A computational model called Casual Probabilistic Reasoning System – CPRS – has been developed (9, 10). The basic architecture of the system is presented in Figure 2.

The system basically consists of two major procedures: (1) Model Construction and (2) Evidence Propagation.

The Model Construction part allows an expert to design a casual graph through a knowledge elicitation programme, and input associated conditional probabilities. It also allows us to construct the graph directly out of data by applying the polytree algorithm (11). The key idea behind the polytree algorithm is to use the Chow–Liu algorithm in order to produce the maximum weight spanning tree, and then to identify directionality for all branches of the tree.

The Evidence Propagation part takes as an input the stored graph ("belief network") and when evidence is observed for any specified node, the system propagates it through the cliques in the graph. As a result of propagation a set of new marginal probabilities is found.

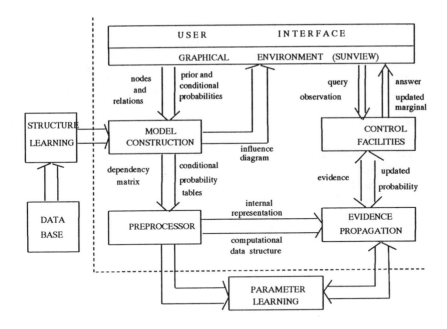

Figure 2   The architecture of the CPRS model.

4   MEDICAL EXAMPLE

The main data relates to 6,000 patients at a hospital in Scotland[1] suffering from acute abdominal pain. For each patient the records showed 33 symptoms or conditions with corresponding values, and the final diagnosis is to one of nine diseases or diagnostic groups. For details see Appendix 1.

5   RESULTS

We now present results of performance of both models. In each case the training set was 4,387 patients' records, and 2,000 were used as the testing set.

---

[1]   Data were used with permission of Mr. S. J. Nixon of the Western General Hospital, Edinburgh and Mr A. A. Gunn formerly of the Bangour Hospital, Roxburgh, where the data were originally collected.

5.1   The G&T Model

The results of application of the G&T system are shown below. Table 1 illustrates a specimen set of combinations of relevant symptoms, with estimated probabilities and upper and lower confidence limits for a diagnostic group (in this case Perforated Peptic Ulcer – PPU) chosen from a training set of 4,387 patients.

Table 2 shows the overall accuracy of the approach applied to the testing set of 2,000 patients.

Here the column headed N gives the number of past patients who had this combination of symptoms (their meaning can be found in the Appendix 1); the column headed D shows how many of them had the disease. The column headed P shows the ratio D/N, which can be used as an estimate of the probability p that a new patient with this combination of symptoms will have the disease. The upper and lower confidence limits for p are given in the columns L and U respectively.

Table 1:   Selected combinations of symptoms for perforated peptic ulcer.

D=Perforated Peptic Ulcer						D	N	P	L	U
Combinations										
(1)	29/0	32/1	26/2			0	13	0.000	0.000	0.250
(2)	29/0	32/1	$\overline{26/2}$			47	79	0.595	0.470	0.710
(3)	29/0	$\overline{32/1}$				10	105	0.095	0.086	0.112
(4)	$\overline{29/0}$	32/1	29/1			12	258	0.047	0.044	0.053
(5)	$\overline{29/0}$	32/1	$\overline{29/1}$			2	4	0.500	0.060	0.940
(6)	$\overline{29/0}$	$\overline{32/1}$	26/9			5	142	0.035	0.029	0.048
(7)	$\overline{29/0}$	$\overline{32/1}$	$\overline{26/9}$	26/4		4	197	0.020	0.017	0.029
(8)	$\overline{29/0}$	$\overline{32/1}$	$\overline{26/9}$	$\overline{26/4}$	23/1	3	140	0.021	0.016	0.034
(9)	$\overline{29/0}$	$\overline{32/1}$	$\overline{26/9}$	$\overline{26/4}$	$\overline{23/1}$	5	3449	0.001	0.001	0.002

Table 2: Accuracy of diagnoses – G&T.

Computer Diagnoses vs Final Diagnoses									
Comp. Diag . (Treshold 11.5)	Final Diagnoses								
	APP	DIV	PPU	NAP	CHO	INO	PAN	RCO	DYS	Total
APP	121	0	6	118	3	5	0	0	6	259
DIV	1	9	2	19	1	2	0	1	0	35
PPU	2	0	21	13	1	0	0	0	5	42
NAP	47	9	0	753	17	12	0	23	33	894
CHO	2	1	2	47	121	5	0	4	18	200
INO	1	6	0	52	2	55	0	0	11	127
PAN	0	0	2	16	5	2	1	2	3	31
RCO	2	2	0	69	1	0	0	73	0	147
DYS	2	0	3	82	20	5	0	5	148	265
Total	178	27	36	1169	171	86	1	108	224	2000

5.2 The CPRS Model

Given available data the polytree algorithm (Pearl, 1988) has been applied to construct the belief network, and then the 'message-passing' technique has been used for evidence propagation.

5.2.1 The Polytree Algorithm

An algorithm proposed by J. Pearl developed in the assumption that underlying distribution can be approximated by a dependency tree consists of two steps: the first is to construct a skeleton undirected causal tree and the second is to identify the direction of the branches of the tree by using a series of tests for independence.

A   Skeleton Tree

In the first step the main idea is to use a notion of tree dependence to approximate the underlying probability distribution data. In particular, the algorithm allows to find the best approximation of a n-order distribution by a product of (n–1) second order distributions. The main result can be formulated as follows.

A probability distribution of a tree dependence $P_t(X_1, X_2, ..., X_n)$ is an optimum approximation to "real" distribution $P(X_1, X_2, ..., X_n)$ if and only if its dependence tree t has maximum weight, where the weight is determined by the mutual information $I(X_i, X_j)$ between two variables X_i and X_j:

$$I(X_i, X_j) = \sum_{X_i, X_j} P(X_i, X_j) \tag{1}$$

It has been proved by Chow and Liu that maximise the total branch weight is equivalent to minimise the Kullback-Liebler measure

$$D(P, P_t) = \sum_X P(X_1, X_2, ..., X_n) \log \frac{P(X_1, X_2, ..., X_n)}{P_t(X_1, X_2, ..., X_n)} \tag{2}$$

This measure can be interpreted as the difference between two distributions: it is always positive when the distributions are different and is zero when they are identical. Here is the formal algorithm for constructing the maximum weight spanning tree (MWST):

There are $N(N-1)/2$ pairs of $I(X_i, X_j)$, and the algorithm terminates when $(N-1)$ branches have been selected, at which point, the dependency tree has been constructed.

```
FOR i = 1 to N–1 DO
   FOR j = i+1 to N DO
   BEGIN
      find out all second-order probability distributions P(Xi, Xj)
      calculate mutual information measure I(Xi, Xj)
   END
Branches No = 0;
WHILE (Branches No < (N–1))
   select two variables Xi, Xj who have largest I(Xi, Xj)
   add the branch (Xi, Xj) to the tree
   IF (there is a loop in the tree)
      delete the branch (Xi, Xj)
ELSE
   Branches No = Branches No + 1;
   print out the branch (Xi, Xj)
END
```

Algorithm A

B   Recovering Directionality

Having constructed the skeleton tree the next task is to recover the directions of the branches. According to the polytree algorithm we consider each internal node (the node that has more than one neighbour), and apply a dependency test. That is, if, say, X_k is an internal node and has at least two neighbours X_i and X_j, then we try to establish whether X_i and X_j are marginally independent. If they are, then we assign directions from X_i to X_k and from X_j to X_k.

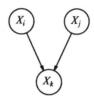

Figure 3

If, however, X_i and X_j are not marginally independent then there are two possible assignments: from X_k to X_i and X_j, or from X_k to to X_i and X_j to X_k.

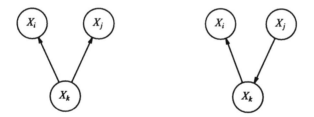

Figure 4

We repeat this procedure for all possible combinations of pairs for each internal node, and assign directions when appropriate. Some assignments, however, may be inconsistent (the arrows in a branch may go in both directions) due to the different types of dependency structure. As it has been shown, the only one type of dependency can be uniquely identified and therefore, only a "partial" recovery may be possible.

As an independency test, we can continue to use the mutual information measure. This time we can exploit the fact that if X_i and X_j are independent then the measure is asymptotically distributed as noncentral χ^2 with $(r-1)(c-1)$ degrees of freedom, where r and c are the number of values of variables X_i and X_j respectively.

The algorithm for identifying direction is as follows:

```
FOR i = 1 to N DO
BEGIN
  IF (Xi has more than one neighbour)
  THEN put Xi in MULTIPLE_SET
END
FOR each Xi in MULTIPLE_SET
BEGIN
  FOR any pair of neighbours (Xj, Xk) of Xi DO
  BEGIN
    IF (Xj and Xk are independent)
    THEN
      2I is distributed as χ² with (r–1)(c–1) degrees of freedom
      (where I is the mutual information measure)
      Xj → Xi, Xk → Xi
    ELSE
    BEGIN
      IF (Xj → Xi)
      THEN
        Xi → Xk
      IF (Xk → Xi)
      THEN
        Xi → Xj
    END
  END
END
```

Algorithm B

For computational convenience we use the following formula:

$$I = \sum_i \sum_j X_{ij} \log X_{ij} - \sum_i X_i \log X_i - \sum_j X_j \log X_j + N \log N \qquad (3)$$

where N is the size of the database under consideration ans X_{ij}, X_i, X_j are the frequencies of occurrencies in the database.

Note that the algorithm we used is slightly different from the one described in In our calculations we only check whether a node is an internal node, and if it is we immediately apply the independency test. In Pearl's setting the algorithm also checks whether the internal node is multiple parents node. The algorithm then checks whether pairs have partial recovered connections and does the independency test.

According to Chow-Liu algorithm the information measures between all pairs of variables have been calculated and the maximum weight spanning tree (MWST) has been constructed by ordering the measure ans choosing only those branches that did not form a loop. The resulting table for 33 branches is given in Table 3.

Figure 5 shows a MWST constructed on the base of those results, where the node No. 34 (diagnostic node) has been chosen as a root of the tree.

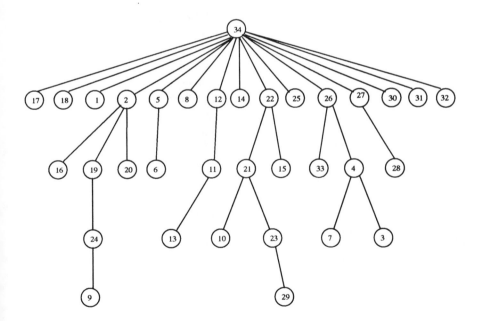

Figure 5 Skeleton Tree

Table 3: Branches of the skeleton Tree.

Order	Selected Branches	Information Measure
1	(3, 4)	0.968999
2	(4, 26)	0.752362
3	(26, 34)	0.466640
4	(19, 24)	0.407164
5	(2, 34)	0.253484
6	(5, 6)	0.162493
7	(21, 23)	0.136150
8	(26, 33)	0.097465
9	(21, 22)	0.089500
10	(5, 34)	0.088761
11	(31, 34)	0.086216
12	(27, 34)	0.085424
13	(2, 19)	0.082851
14	(22, 34)	0.082084
15	(32, 34)	0.078212
16	(9, 24)	0.076851
17	(11, 12)	0.070648
18	(14, 34)	0.067856
19	(27, 28)	0.067694
20	(25, 34)	0.067312
21	(2, 20)	0.064471
22	(10, 21)	0.059096
23	(4, 7)	0.058322
24	(17, 34)	0.057519
25	(23, 29)	0.049169
26	(2, 16)	0.046241
27	(8, 34)	0.046079
28	(11, 13)	0.044869
29	(1, 34)	0.038894
30	(12, 34)	0.036183
31	(15, 22)	0.031611
32	(18, 34)	0.031181
33	(30, 34)	0.019067

C   Directions on the MWST

Using the test for independence described above we can assign directions to the skeleton tree. However, there are some problems arise in assiging directions to the MWST. For example, some directions are clearly meaningless from medical point of view. In order to avoid this a medical expert's advice has been sought and as a result of the consultation the skeleton tree has been pruned by choosing a threshold (I = 0.065). After that the test for independence for all pairs of variables X_i and X_j of each internal node has been applied. That is when the 0.005% values of χ^2 with respective degrees of freedom is less than the doubled mutual infromation measure 2I, then we accept the hypothesis of independence between variable X_i and X_j. In some cases where both directions can be assigned to the same branch, we did not assign the directions at all. For these branches where the algorithm could not assign any directions we use the doctor's advice and impose the directions (dashed lines) suggested by them. The corresponding pruned casual tree is represented in Figure 6.

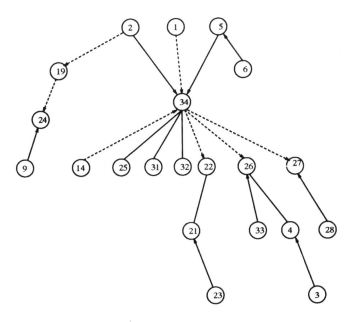

Figure 6 Pruned Polytree.

5.2.3 Discussion

There is a number of problems associated with the approach. First of all as it has been said some of the directions on the tree are meaningless from medical point of view. They certainly do not represent "casual" directions. The most we can say about some of them that they reflect "commonality". For example, the link from node 3 (Paint-site Onset) to node 4 (Pain-site present). Secondly, some links have arrows going in both directions. For example, branch 11 ↔ 12 or 21 ↔ 22. Therefore, for these links the directions can only be assigned arbitrary. This problem has been mentioned before and it is connected with non-unique recovery due to different types of dependencies. Thirdly, some nodes have far too many parent nodes. For example, the disease node has nine parent nodes in out polytree. In order to specify the conditional probabilities for the node, more than 6 million probabilities are needed. It is unrealistic to propagate evidence using this amount of information. The problem can be avoided by introducing a threshold, or to employ the idea developed in the G&T system. In the latter case we need to estimate combinations of the variables which actually occur in the database. The design of such modification constitutes an important path for future research.

6   CONCLUSIONS

Two computational models have been described and applied to a large medical database. The following conclusions can be made out of experience with the G&T model.

From a very complicated database it proved possible to identify, by a purely statistical method, selections of symptoms which were immediately identified by doctors as being relevant to the diagnoses. Using these symptoms it was possible to estimate probabilities by a strict application of Bayes' theorem, without assuming independence. The probabilities were estimated entirely from past data, without requiring subjective estimates. The method is extremely straightforward and easy to explain, and confidence limits are given for every estimate. General computer architecture has been described which could be applied to any database.

The latest experiments show that the method can actually "travel" from one area to another. That is the combination of symptoms with corresponding probabilities found in one geographical area can be transferred into another area with a different population, and applied to a different set of data. The accuracy achieved by the system is on the same level (70%) (12). This is quite different from the "simple Bayes" method which depends upon prior probability distribution and therefore the results will change from one place to another.

As regards the complexity of the calculations, the number of operations per probability calculated is the order of V*S*P, where V is the number of variables, S is the average number of states per variable, and P is a number of past patients. This order of magnitude does not increase exponentially or depend on the total state space.

The CPRS model can perform its inference in linear time with respect to the size of the graph (the sum of the sizes of the nodes, the arcs and the probabilities), provided that it is so-called a singly connected graph. But in general it is known that the problem of inference for belief networks is NP-hard (13). Unfortunately, in our practical application despite using the directed tree structure, we had to estimate a lot of probabilities. There are several ways to address this problem. One method is similar to the basic idea of the G&T approach. That is to consider only those probabilities which actually occur in our database. Another way is to use approximate algorithms, for example, a method called stochastic simulation (14). A computational system called STOSS has been developed and described elsewhere (15).

In our case we actually used a heuristic technique and simplified the topology of the tree be deleting some branches according to doctors' recommendations.

In general both models have a similar level of the diagnostic accuracy, and this level is comparable with the performance of doctors.

7   ACKNOWLEDGEMENTS

I am greatly indebted to Mr S. J. Nixon MB, ChB, BSc, FRCS, of the General Surgical Unit, Western General Hospital, Edinburgh; Mr A. A. Gunn, MB, ChM, FRCS, formerly of the Bangour Hospital, Roxburgh for their expert advice and for making available data originally collected at Bangour Hospital. I also wish to thank Mr Zhiyuan Luo and Miss Yiqun Gu for useful discussions and some results with both systems.

REFERENCES

(1) Buchanan, B.G. and Shortliffe, E.H. (1984) Rule-based Expert Systems; the MYCIN Experiment of the Stanford Heuristic Programming Project, Reading, Mass.: Addison-Wesley.

(2) Cheeseman, P. (1986) Probabilistic versus Fuzzy Reasoning, Uncertainty in Artificial Intelligence, L.N. Kanal and J.F. Lemmer (Eds.), pp. 85–102.

(3) Duda, R.O., Gashing, J. and Hart, P.E. (1979) Model Design in the Prospector Consultant System for Mineral Exploration, Expert Systems in the Micro-electronic Age, Edinburgh University Press.

(4) Gammerman, A. and Thatcher, A.R. (1990) Bayesian Inference in an Expert System without Assuming Independence, Advances in Artificial Intelligence (ed. by M.C. Golumbic), pp. 182–195, Springer-Vering.

(5) Pearl, J. (1986) Fusion, Propagation and Structuring in Belief Networks, Artificial Intelligence, Vol. 29, pp. 241–288.

(6) Lauritzen, S.L. and Spiegelhalter, D.J. (1988) Local Computations with Probabilities on Graphical Structures and their Application to Expert Systems, J. R. Statist., Soc. B, Vol. 50, pp. 157–224, with discussion.

(7) Thatcher, A.R, (1988) Computer Models of Probabilistic Reasoning: Bayes Theorem without Assuming Independence, Technical Report, Vol. 88/1, Heriot-Watt University, Edinburgh.

(8) Spiegelhalter, D.J. (1986) Probabilistic Reasoning in Predictive Expert Systems, Uncertainty in Artificial Intelligence, L.N. Kanal and J.F. Lemmer (Eds.), pp. 47–67.

(9) Gammerman, A. and Crabbe, W. (1987) Computational models of probabilistic reasoning in expert systems: a casual probabilistic reasoning system, Technical Report 87/16, Computer Science Department, Heriot-Watt University, Edinburgh.

(10) Gammerman, A., Luo, Z. and Aitken, C.G.G., (1991) A Computational Reasoning System for Mixed Probabilistic Models, DOSES Project B6, LIKELY Technical Report, Edinburgh.

(11) Pearl, J. (1988) Probabilistic in Intelligent Systems: Networks of Plausible Inference Morgan Kaufmann Publishers, Inc., San Mateo, California.

(12) de Dombal, T. (1991) Personal Communication.

(13) Cooper, G.F. (1989) Current research directions in the development of expert systems based on belief networks, Applied Stochastic Models and Data Analysis, Vol. 5, pp. 39–52.

(14) Pearl, J. (1987) Evidential Reasoning using Stochastic Simulation of Causal Models, Artificial Intelligence, Vol. 32, pp. 245–257.

(15) Luo, Z. and Gammerman, A. (1990) A Stochastic Simulation System for Causal Models, Proc. of 3rd IPUM, Paris, France.

Appendix 1

List of Diagnostic Groups

1.   Diagnostic groups

Diagnostic Groups		
Group No.	Diagnosis	Abbrev.
1	Appendicitis	APP
2	Diverticulitis	DIV
3	Perforated Peptic Ulcer	PPU
4	Non-specific Abdominal Pain	NSAP
5	Cholisistitis	CHO
5	Intestinal Obstruction	INO
6	Pancreatitis	PAN
8	Renal Colic	RCO
9	Dyspepsia	DYS

List of symptoms with their values

Symptom	Values (No.)
1. Sex	male (0), female (1)
2. Age	0-9 (0), 10-19 (1), 20-29 (2), 30-39 (3) 40-49 (4), 50-59 (5), 60-69 (6), 70+ (7)
3. Pain-site Onset	right upper quadrant (0), left upper quadrant (1), right lower quadrant (2) left lower quadrant (3), upper half (4), lower half (5), right half (6), left half (7) central (8), general (9), right loin (10), left loin (11), epigastric (12)
4. Pain-site Present	right upper quadrant (0), left upper quadrant (1), right lower quadrant (2) left lower quadrant (3), upper half (4), lower half (5), right half (6), left half (7) central (8), general (9), right loin (10), left loin (11), epigastric (12), pain settled (13)
5. Aggravating Factors	movement (0), coughing (1), inspiration (2), food (3), other (4), nil (5)
6. Relieving Factors	lying still (0), vomiting (1), antacids (2), milk/food (3), other (4), nil (5)
7. Progress of Pain	getting better (0), no change (1), getting worse (2)
8. Duration of Pain	under 12 hours (0), 12-24 hours (1), 24-48 hours (2), over 48 hours (3)
9. Type of Pain	steady (0), intermittent (1), colicky (2), sharp (3)
10. Severity of Pain	moderate (0), severe (1)
11. Nausea	nausea present (0), no nausea (1)
12. Vomiting	present (0), no vomiting (1)
13 Anorexia	present (0), normal appetite (1)
14. Indigestion	history of dyspepsia (0), no history of dyspepsia (1)
15. Jaundice	history jaundice (0), no history of jaundice (1)
16. Bowel Habit	no change (0), constipated (1), diarrhoea (2), blood (3), mucous (4)
17. Micturation	normal (0), frequent (1), dysuria (2), haematuria (3), dark urine (4)
18. Previous Pain	similar pain before (0), no similar pain before (1)
19. Previous Surgery	yes (0), none (1)
20. Drugs	being taken (0), not being taken (1)
21. Mood	normal (0), distressed (1), anxious (2)
22. Colour	normal (0), pale (1), flushed (2), jaundiced (3), cyanosed (4)
23. Abdominal Movements	normal (0), poor/nil (1), visible peristalsis (2)
24. Abdominal Scar	present (0), absent (1)
25. Abdominal Distension	present (0), absent (1)
26. Site of Tenderness	right upper quadrant (0), left upper quadrant (1), right lower quadrant (2) left lower quadrant (3), upper half (4), lower half (5), right half (6), left half (7) central (8), general (9), right loin (10), left loin (11), epigastric (12), none (13)
27. Rebound	present (0), absent (1)
28. Guarding	present (0), absent (1)
29. Rigidity	present (0), absent (1)
30. Abdominal Masses	present (0), absent (1)
31. Murphy's Test	positive (0), negative (1)
32. Bowel Sounds	normal (0), decreased (1), increased (2)
33. Rectal Examination	tender left side (0), tender right side (1), generally tender (2) mass felt (3), normal (4)

11 A general numerical approach to the benchmark problems in defeasible reasoning

S. F. Roehrig*
Carnegie Mellon University, The Heinz School of Public Policy and
Management

1   INTRODUCTION

Reasoning with incomplete or uncertain information is so common that it is second nature to all of us. The means by which each of us make decisions under these conditions remain largely inaccessible, despite considerable research effort, but this fact has not prevented the investigation of a number of accounts by which computer-based systems might reach reasonable conclusions. Both logical and numerical methods have been proposed (see e.g. [Buchanan and Shortliffe 1984, Gale 1986, Genesereth and Nilsson 1988, Kanal and Lemmer 1986, Pearl 1988]), the best of each offering credible performance in a range of situations where complete information is unavailable. As a means of comparing different methods, a set of benchmark problems in defeasible reasoning has been assembled by a group of researchers in the field [Loui-1989]. In this paper we show how path analysis [Glymour et al.1987, Wright 1934, Wright 1960], used as a method for structuring reasoning under uncertainty [Kimbrough and Roehrig 1990], can be applied with good results to a number of these benchmark problems. Another recent paper [Kimbrough 1991] illustrates a qualitative method applied to many of these same problems, and comparison of the two methods is instructive.

The benchmark problems offer a surprising variety of situations where conflicting statements must be weighed against one another. In each case a coherent framework is sought, in which each piece of evidence can comfortably fit, in which the relationships between entities are maintained according to the given statements, and from which useful conclusions can be drawn. The problems are important because they represent typical situations in which we

*   This research was performed while the author was employed by the U.S. Coast Guard R&D Center, Avery Point, Groton, CT. Their support is greatly appreciated.

might find ourselves in everyday life – there is nothing arcane or outlandish about them – and are solved with varying degrees of success by humans, apparently without the aid of formal logic or numerical calculi [Harman 1986].

The problems are liberally spiced with words like "tends", "usually", and "probably". Many would argue that people deal comfortably with such terms, so it should be possible to manipulate them coherently in a computer program in their original qualitative form. But in problems of substance (and many of the benchmarks verge on this) it seems one must inevitably ask further questions. Is this "tends" stronger than that 'usually'? Do two 'tends' make up for a 'probably'? By asking many such questions we get closer to some other familiar ground, namely probability theory. Several of the many approaches to probability rely on just such repeated comparison and hair-splitting [Smithson 1989]. It seems reasonable, then, that we might as well go the extra distance right at the outset and ask for quantification in terms of probability.

It is well known that many (most?) people exhibit the artefacts of 'innumeracy' by making well-documented blunders in estimating and manipulating probabilities [Kahneman et al. 1982]. But do we know that people are more reliable in coherently organizing and manipulating the qualitative substitutes? In any event, what of the situation in which knowledge comes to us numerically in the first place? Is the transformation of probabilities (e.g., frequency of occurrence) into the qualitative terms more easily accomplished than the reverse?

These questions will not be answered here – the numerical path analytic approach will simply be illustrated in the context of the benchmark problems. Any method, numerical or symbolic, will have pros and cons in expressiveness, in the assumptions made to operationalise it, and in any computer implementation. The intent here is to show that path analysis has the ability to provide the required coherent framework, and can be used to reach correct conclusions.

If the qualitative terms are quantified, then, what forms will they take? The sentence 'Usually, x' very simply becomes $P(x) = p$ for some appropriately large value of p. The accuracy of a stated value of p can surely be questioned. The proposition x may be one of a repeated series of trials, or may be a once-in-a-lifetime thing. Various formulations of probability address these extremes, but while skirting this issue as much as possible, it can be said that, just as a rough ordering of phrases like 'tends', 'usually' and 'probably' is enough to make sense out of some problems in a qualitative scheme, extreme precision in estimating probabilities is not necessarily required to produce correct conclusions in a numerical framework. It might be noted that determining the sensitivity of a problem to the numerical estimates is in general easily accomplished. This may be far less true for qualitative systems (though logic graphs [Kimbrough 1986] may be an important exception).

After constructing the casual tree we can use our training set in order to supply all necessary prior and conditional probabilities. At this stage when we obtained a qualitative structure in the form of casual tree, and quantitative information concerning this tree, the *model construction* phase is finished. Now in order to make diagnosis we can exploit the *evidence propagation* procedure.

5.2.2 Computer Diagnosis

Having constructed a casual tree with associated probabilities we can use one of the propagation techniques developed in order to make diagnosis. That is we propagate observations of symptoms of a new patient through this tree and re-assess the probabilities of the diagnostic node. The node has nine values and shall have nine probabilities for each patient from the testing set. As a "computer diagnosis" then we take the highest probability and interpret it as a diagnosis for this patient. Having a sample of 2,000 patients we can then evaluate our accuracy by comparing the results with final diagnoses given by the doctors, see Table 4.

Table 4: Comparison between Computer Diagnoses and Final Diagnoses.

Computer Diagnosis vs Final Diagnosis									
	Computer Diagnosis								
Final Diagnosis	APP	DIV	PPU	NAP	CHO	INO	PAN	RCO	DYS	Total
APP	178	1	3	59	0	9	2	0	7	259
DIV	2	14	0	6	0	9	0	0	4	35
PPU	2	1	19	2	3	6	6	0	3	42
NAP	106	20	3	683	11	21	0	16	34	894
CHO	2	0	4	7	128	14	4	4	37	200
INO	8	14	4	22	6	59	1	2	11	127
PAN	0	0	2	1	6	1	8	0	13	31
RCO	3	3	0	27	6	12	2	92	2	147
DYS	4	1	7	27	22	4	5	4	191	265
Total	305	54	42	834	182	135	28	118	302	2000

There is a large class of qualitative remarks which are of the form 'If x, then likely y'. This class has been the source of considerable confusion in attempts to develop a 'quantified logic'. Attaching a numerical confidence factor to a material implication needs to be done with great care – what will it mean in those cases where x is either not true or unlikely? A better numerical interpretation is in terms of the conditional probability $P(y \mid x)$. If the case where x is not true is important, then $P(y \mid x)$ is also required. At least in this interpretation, what is being asked for is clear.

There is the problem of dealing with defaults (e.g., 'Normally x'). Typically, we should take the probability of x to be a number closely approaching 1.0, so that it will swamp any other countering proposition having a high, but not default, probability. This is a viable approach, and Pearl [Pearl 1988] makes good use of it in his analysis of the Yale shooting problem. We will show in some of the analyses to follow that default assumptions, and their defeat when additional information becomes available, can be handled capably and probabilistically correctly by the method of path analysis.

As mentioned above, there are many situations where data will come to us in the form of a distribution; that is, as a list of co-occurrences of propositions. In fact, for path analysis, which is based on standardised regression on data, this is the ideal form. These situations, along with those where summarizing probabilities are given, and also hybrids of these, will need to be dealt with in a uniform way. Our proposal is this: if the distribution is available, either explicitly as data or implicitly as in, e.g., a Bayesian network [Pearl 1988], use it; if only (conditional) probabilities are available, use an imputation scheme to recover a distribution which matches the probabilities. Our choice for this imputation is maximum entropy [Cheeseman 1983]. This technique generates a distribution which agrees with all given data, but assumes no additional information (in the sense of Shannon and Weaver).

The objection might be raised that dealing with a complete probability distribution over a large number of propositions tends to get exponentially large. This objection has been answered effectively in the more recent literature on network-based probability models [Pearl 1988, Shafer and Pearl 1990]. The basic rebuttal is that there is no direct relationship between most propositions; those which are causally or otherwise connected will give rise to conditional probabilities quantifying that connection, but independence is the norm rather than the exception. Network-like structures (a class to which path diagrams belong) are routinely used to make explicit these independence assumptions, and network-based data structures are used instead of a joint probability table, providing a radically more efficient storage medium.

With this brief introduction, we now move on to some concrete problems, hoping to flesh out (by example) the method of path analysis as applied to inference under uncertainty. It is assumed that the reader has some grasp of path analysis, or at any rate that simple regression and correlation pose no great conceptual obstacles. As mentioned above, the problems which follow come from Loui 1989.

2 FIATS ARE FAST?

Fiats are North Italian cars
North Italian cars tend to be fast
Sports cars tend to be fast
Fiats tend to be slow
Fred's Fiat is a sports car

From this evidence we wish to know if Fred's Fiat is fast. To handle this problem probabilistically, it is obviously necessary to quantify 'tends'. We take the position here that 'tends' may not always mean exactly the same probability; slightly different degrees of belief might equally well be verbalised as 'tends'. Later we will examine some situations where each occurrence of 'tends' is given exactly the same probability, but in general we don't require it. Qualitative systems, on the other hand, must either regard each such occurrence as equally compelling, or ask the person providing the information to revise his statements using a graded vocabulary of degrees of belief. Using (real) numbers for degrees of belief seems a much more straightforward approach.

What we can legitimately ask for here, then, are the numbers P(fast | North Italian), P(fast | Sports car), and P(fast | Fiat). We know from the first line that P(Italian | Fiat) = 1. Where would these numbers come from? The person who made the statements above might have drawn upon his own subjective experience, the experience of others ('I remember Ted telling me '), or perhaps‧ they were the result of database queries at the department of motor vehicles. For the first two, subjective estimates of the conditionals are likely to be the most information we could hope to obtain. Were we lucky enough to be in the last situation, a complete sample distribution could be assembled. (We assume that Fred's licence number is unknown, so that some inference is actually required.)

Assume for now that by one means or another the following joint distribution is made available to us, where a 1 indicates the predicate is true, while a 0 means it is false. Each column in the table should be thought of as an observation of the co-occurrence of the predicates.

Predicate	Var.	
N. Ital.	ni	1 1 1 1 1 1 1 1 1 1 1 0 0 0 0
Fiat	fi	1 1 1 1 1 1 1 1 0 0 0 0 0 0 0
Spts Car	sc	1 1 1 1 1 0 0 0 1 1 1 0 1 1 0 0
Fast	fa	1 1 1 0 0 0 0 0 1 1 1 1 1 1 1 1

From this table, the relevent probabilities are

$$P \, (ni \mid fi) \quad = \quad 1$$
$$P \, (fa \mid ni) \quad = \quad 7/12$$
$$P \, (fa \mid sc) \quad = \quad 4/5$$
$$P \, (fa \mid fi) \quad = \quad 3/8$$

showing that the spirit of the problem is correctly captured.

There are many possible path diagrams involving four variables, but for this problem it seems natural to consider the following one. Upper case letters are used to represent standardised variables (i.e., linearly transformed to have zero means and unit variances), but the assignment of letters to propositions is the same as in the table above. Also, correlations and residual variables, to be discussed below, are suppressed from this diagram. Here we show only assumed causal relationships.

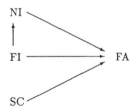

The reason for choosing this diagram is that we are given four 'clues', each resulting in an assumed causal connection between propositions. If we are prohibited from examining the matter further, or if we can provide no intuition of our own, there is no basis for adding more arcs. There is no arc joining FI and SC, for example, because there is no direct connection between Fiats and sports cars provided by the problem statement, and it is unclear a priori in which way such an arc would be directed.

The path analysis proceeds by standardising the variables to zero means and unit variances, followed by a simple regression and correlation analysis. For the data at hand, it happens that there is considerable interaction between

FI and SC, reflected in their conditional dependence given FA. The upshot of this dependence is that evidence concerning FI and SC combine nonlinearly to produce belief in FA. Thus the regression must incorporate the product term FI.SC which we will call FS[1]. The complete path diagram is shown below, along with the scaling of the variables. The propositional variables ni, fi, sc and fa range between 0 and 1 (false to true, or total disbelief to total belief), while the standardized variables NI, FI, SC and FA range correspondingly between the limits shown. Linear interpolation will map any partial belief in a proposition to the corresponding value of a standardised variable (examples will follow).

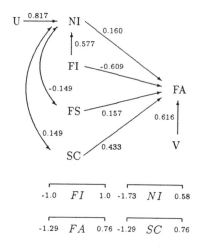

The complete path diagram has several additional features. The curved arcs represent correlations (with numerical measures juxtaposed). The absence of a correlation arc in the diagram indicates that the correlation is zero. Two additional variables, U and V, have been added. Since the method of path analysis insists that the system being considered be causally closed, these residual variables are added to indicate influence from any and all other unspecified factors. The coefficients of the paths originating at U and V are related to the variance in the predicted variables (NI and FA) which is unaccounted for by the predictors. They may be useful as diagnostics in judging the causal completeness of the network structure, but that issue will not be addressed here. The straight-line paths now have path coefficients.

---

1   This is by no means unusual. As an extreme example, consider a simple binary and circuit. The probability that the output is one is just the product of the probabilities that the two inputs are one.

There is nothing special about any of these numbers; the correlations are simply that, and the path coefficients are merely coefficients in linear equations which predict the values of dependent variables from known values of some independent variables. For instance, NI can be predicted from a known value of FA (and so ni from fi). Similarly, a predicted value for FA can be obtained from values for NI, FI and SC. It has been shown in [Kimbrough and Roehrig 1990] that these predicted values, when unstandardised, are exactly the probabilities which would be obtained from a conventional probability analysis.

Numerically, if FI is at its maximum value 1.0, then the predicted value for NI is this value times the coefficient for the path from FI to NA, that is, $0.58 \times 1.0 = 0.58$. Note this is the maximum value for NA, which simply shows that a car is indeed North Italian if it is a Fiat. Going beyond the simple case of certain knowledge, any partial belief in the 'Fiat-ness' of a car can be mapped into a corresponding degree of belief in its 'North Italian-ness'. For example, if the probability that a car is a Fiat is 0.6, i.e., fi = 0.6, then this number is standardised according to

$$FI = Stand(fi)$$
$$= P(fi) \ (max \ (FI) - min \ (FI)) + min \ (FI)$$
$$= 0.6 \ (1.0 - (-1.0)) + (-1.0) = 0.2$$

so that $NI = 0.58 \times 0.2 = 0.116$, which upon un-standardising gives ni = 0.8, the appropriate probability that the car is North Italian. [Kimbrough and Roehrig 1990] shows that this simple technique is probabilistically correct, taking into account both $P(ni \mid fi)$ and $P(ni \mid \neg fi)$.

In this same way, if we are given probabilities for ni, fi and sc, we may arrive at the probability of fa. But in the benchmark problem we know only that Fred's Fiat is a sports car. To use this, and only this, information, we can use a device which illustrates one of the beauties of path analysis: the path diagram can be collapsed so that the influence of ni is incorporated only implicitly [Li 1977]. The path from FI through NI to FA can be merged with that from FI to FA, resulting in the following diagram.

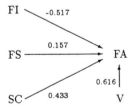

Note that the coefficient for the residual variable V is unchanged – there is no more or less information available concerning FA. Also note that there are no correlation arcs in this diagram; the actual correlations in this example happen to be zero. The scaling remains the same, so it is now easy to decide if Fred's Fiat is fast. Starting with fi = 1 and sc = 1, standardise to FI = 1.0 and SC = 0.77, so that FS = 0.77. Now multiply by the the corresponding path coefficients and sum, yielding FA = –0.06. Unstandardising gives fa = 3/5, that is, there is a 3/5 chance that the Fiat in question is fast.

This result is in total agreement with the data. What path analysis also enables, though, is the straightforward calculation of belief in fa given partial belief in the other propositions. The method subsumes some rather complex calculations involving a considerable number of conditional probabilities and facilitates, through the collapsing mechanism, calculation of probabilities in the absence of probabilistic knowledge about any subset of predictors.

In analysing the problem of Fred's Fiat, we assumed that hard data on the co-occurrence of the four propositions was available. Obviously, this will not always be the case. Whenever it is available, it certainly should be used. But otherwise, we require a distribution which matches whatever probability estimates are available, but which introduces no further information or hidden assumptions. The next benchmark problem will be analysed by assuming only that several conditional probabilities (corresponding to the verb 'tends') are given to us.

3   GARFIELD AND PEOPLE

Cats tend to be aloof
Aloofness tends to indicate dislike of people
Cats tend to like people
Garfield is a cat

Well then, does Garfield like people? To model this scenario using the quantitative method of path analysis, we need at a minimum three conditional probabilities. Let c = cat, a = is aloof, and l = likes people. Then suppose that the following numbers have been given to us:

$$P(a \mid c) = 3/5$$
$$P(l \mid a) = 2/5$$
$$P(l \mid c) = 3/5.$$

To apply path analysis, these probabilities need to be turned into data about the co-occurrence of the three propositions – that is, a sample distribution. As mentioned above, our choice for this task is the maximum entropy method. The conditionals act as constraints in a mathematical programming problem whose objective function is a measure of the entropy or randomness of the distribution. We write P_{cal} for the general entry in the distribution, where c, a and l can take on the values 0 and 1. Thus, e.g., P_{101} represents the value of $P(c = 1, a = 0, l = 1)$. The probability equations are then transformed into constraints using the definition of conditional probability. For instance, the first conditional probability above can be written as

$$\frac{P\,(a,c)}{P\,(c)} = \frac{3}{5}$$

which becomes

$$P\,(a,c) - \frac{3}{5}\,P\,(c) = 0$$

Expanding the marginals in terms of sums, we can write the constraint as

$$\sum_l P_{1l1} - \frac{3}{5} \sum_{al} P_{1al} = 0$$

The other conditionals are rewritten similarly, and an additional constraint enforcing the usual sums-to-one condition is added. The entropy function is

$$H = - \sum_{cal} P_{cal} \, \log P_{cal}$$

Maximising the entropy subject to the known probability constraints (using the MINOS nonlinear programming package [Murtagh and Saunders 1987] or the method of Cheeseman [Cheeseman 1983]) leads to the following distribution;:

$P_{000} = 0.133$	$P_{001} = 0.133$
$P_{010} = 0.193$	$P_{011} = 0.076$
$P_{100} = 0.050$	$P_{101} = 0.136$
$P_{110} = 0.136$	$P_{111} = 0.144$

A data file conforming to this distribution was created and a path analysis performed, assuming a triangular diagram whose arcs are in one-to-one correspondence with the statements in the problem. It resulted in the following:

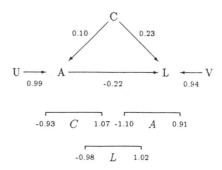

The path diagram enables us to answer the question about Garfield and people. But if that were all, the analysis would clearly have been a waste of time. For what other interpretation of the question 'Does Garfield like people?' can there be than P(l | c)? To extract this from the path diagram is trivial; collapse the path from C to L through A to obtain

and compute the probability of l given that c = 1. This of course comes out to 3/5, which brings us back precisely to where we began.

But there is much more to the full path diagram than this. It can be seen that to collapse the diagram (as was just done), the influence of aloofness was incorporated. Liking people would be a much stronger trait of cats if it were not for the tempering effect of aloofness. The negative path coefficient on the arc A → L is an indication of this effect. If it were known, for instance, that the likelihood that Garfield the cat is aloof is small, this information could be incorporated directly at node A. The net result would be to override the default contribution of aloofness which would ordinarily come from catness.

Path analysis can thus be seen as a way of decomposing the mutual influences of various factors. In the absence of any information beyond the data from which the diagram was constructed, the scaling of the variables encodes the default assumptions. For example, the default level of A is zero, corresponding to the (unstandardised) probability P(A) = 0.55. The addition of any other information forces a revision of our belief structure; the path diagram shows us how to allow for interactions between propositions. Believing that Garfield is a cat causes our belief in his aloofness to increase, which is in turn passed on to node L. The interaction between C and A at L is properly accounted for by the path coefficients.

4   UNIVERSITY STUDENTS

Adults tend to be employed
University students tend to be unemployed
University students tend to be adults
Fred is a university student and an adult

For this problem, we will look at the maximum entropy distribution and two sets of data. Look first at the following:

Predicate	Variable	
Univ. Student	s	1 1 1 1 0 0 0 0 0
Adult	a	1 1 1 0 1 1 1 1 1
Employed	e	1 0 0 0 1 1 1 1 1

we have

$$P(e \mid a) = 3/4$$
$$P(e \mid s) = 1/4$$
$$P(a \mid s) = 3/4$$

so that in this case, 'tends' is quantified uniformly. The completed path diagram is[1]

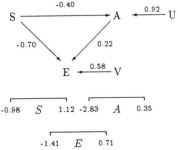

1   The negative path coefficient on the arc from S to A shows that the sign of a coefficient isn't always an indicator of the nature of the causal relation between the unstandardised variables. In this instance there is a net negative correlation between S and A because the data tell us that if we disbelieve that someone is a university student, we should strongly believe she is an adult.

As usual, it is easy to recover all of the relevant probabilities. For example, instantiating s and a to 1.0 yields e = 1/3, our belief that the adult student Fred is employed. To recover P(e | s) it is necessary to collapse the path from S through A to E. This is accomplished by multiplying the path coefficients on the arcs S → A and A → E and adding the result to the coefficient for the arc S → E, resulting in

It appears initially that collapsing to get P(e | a) might not be possible, given the orientation of the arc from S to A. However, it is a fact from path analysis that when there is a single path terminating at a node, its coefficient is also the correlation between the nodes at either end. Thus the original path diagram is equivalent to the following.

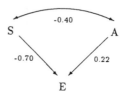

From this diagram it is clear that we can collapse to

$$A \xrightarrow{0.50} E \xleftarrow{0.866} U$$

which yields P(e | a) = 3/4.

We have seen that, given the data above, Fred is probably unemployed (P = 1/3). However, a different set of data can, while remaining faithful to the statements in the problem, necessitate a different conclusion. Consider, for example, the following:

Predicate	Variable	
Univ. Student	s	1 1 1 1 1 0 0 0 0 0
Adult	a	0 0 1 1 1 1 1 0 0 0
Employed	e	0 0 0 1 1 1 0 1 0 0

We have

$$P(e \mid a) = 3/5$$
$$P(e \mid s) = 2/5$$
$$P(a \mid s) = 3/5$$

so that in this case as well, 'tends' is quantified uniformly throughout. It is trivial to compute, though, that in this example, $P(e \mid s,a) = 2/3$.

While path analysis will have no difficulty modelling this new data, it is clear that the word 'tends' in the problem statement is in itself insufficient to draw a firm conclusion. In each of the above examples, 'tends' was quantified uniformly ($P = 3/4$ in the first, $P = 3/5$ in the second), yet the probability that Fred is employed differed remarkably.

It might be argued that these are specially constructed examples in which additional information was subtly incorporated. What, then, does a maximum entropy distribution imply about Fred's employment status? Taking the conditional probabilities as in the first example, but omitting the details, we find that $P(e \mid s,a) = 0.256$. Thus in the absence of additional information, we conclude that Fred is probably unemployed. It is not clear in this example how a qualitative system could argue convincingly one way or the other.

5   DANCERS AND BALLERINAS

Dancers tend not to be ballerinas
Dancers tend to be graceful
Graceful dancers tend to be ballerinas
Noemi is a dancer

In trying to decide if Noemi is a ballerina, there is a tradeoff between directness and specificity. On the one hand, we have the direct negative connection between dancers and ballerinas, but on the other a pair of increasingly specific inferences leads us to a positive connection. There is also the issue of possible hidden assumptions in interpreting the problem. Are graceful dancers a subset of dancers, and are ballerinas necessarily graceful dancers? Or does the problem refer to three distinct categories – dancers, graceful people (who may not be

---

1   It is interesting that under these subset assumptions, requiring each 'tends' to be quantified identically completely specifies it; 'tends' means 'with probability $(\sqrt{5} - 1)/2$'. If ballerinas need not be graceful, requiring equi-probable 'tends' still imposes an upper bound on its value.

dancers), and ballerinas (who could possibly be awkward non-dancers)? We give example data sets and path analyses for both points of view.

Suppose, under the subset interpretation, we have the following[1]:

Predicate	Var.	
Dancer	d	1 1 1 1 1 1 1 1 1 1 0 0 0 0 0
Graceful	g	1 1 1 1 1 1 0 0 0 0 0 0 0 0 0
Ballerina	b	1 1 1 1 0 0 0 0 0 0 0 0 0 0 0

so that

$$P(g \mid d) = 0.6$$
$$P(b \mid g) = 0.667$$
$$P(b \mid d) = 0.4$$

At the right of the table there are five columns filled with zeros, which would seem to be extraneous. Their function is simply to prevent Dancers from having zero variance, which would cause the regression analysis to blow up. This is simply a technicality, and the number of such columns is immaterial so far as the analysis is concerned.

The path diagram is simplicity itself.

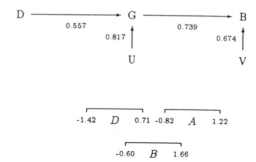

To decide the likelihood that Noemi is a ballerina, it is enough to set d = 1, standardise to X = 0.71, and propagate this value through the two stages of the path to B. We have

$$Z = 0.707 \times 0.577 \times 0.739 = 0.302$$

which when unstandardised yields z = 0.4. It is also possible to collapse the path diagram, simply by multiplying the two path coefficients; the equivalence is obvious, and gives the same result as regressing Z on X directly.

For a different interpretation of the problem, consider this alternate data set.

Predicate	Var.																		
Dancer	d	1 1 1 1 1 1 1 1 1 1 1 1 1 0 0 0 0
Graceful	g	1 1 1 1 1 1 1 0 0 0 0 0 0 0 0 0 0
Ballerina	b	1 1 1 1 0 0 0 1 0 0 0 0 0 0 0 0 0

Note that now there is an instance of an awkward ballerina. In the previous diagram, there were apparently two arcs, corresponding to the second and third statements in the problem. Implicit in that diagram, though, was a third arc joining dancers and ballerinas, which was formed by the combination of the two explicit arcs. For the new data, the third arc must be shown in its own right, since now we don't assume the subset relationships.

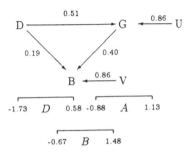

This diagram looks structurally identical to that for University Students, but its application in answering the problem is different. Whereas in University Students, both Student and Adult were instantiated, here we know only that Noemi is a dancer. Thus to decide if she is a ballerina, we can only instantiate the node D. Propagating belief in D, both directly to B and through G to B yields the correct result, namely that she is a ballerina with probability 5/12. This is equivalent to collapsing the path diagram to

which of course gives the same result. Here again, it is easy to incorporate any additional information, for example in the form of partial belief in the gracefulness of Noemi.

6   NICE-GUY LAWYERS

Lawyers tend to be Republican and nice
Republicans tend to be conservative
Conservatives tend to be not-nice
Dave is a conservative Republican lawyer

To determine if Dave is nice, we assume the following data.

Predicate	Var.	
Lawyer	l	1 1 1 1 1 1 1 1 1 1 0 0 0 0 0 0
Repub.	r	1 1 1 0 1 1 1 0 0 0 1 0 0 0 0 0
Cons.	c	1 1 1 1 1 0 0 0 0 0 0 0 0 0 0 0
Nice	n	0 0 0 1 1 1 1 1 1 1 0 0 0 0 0 0

From this table, the relevent probabilities are

$$P(r \mid l) = 3/5$$
$$P(n \mid l) = 7/10$$
$$P(c \mid r) = 4/7$$
$$P(\neg n \mid c) = 3/5$$

There is a slight dilemma here, in that the evidence contained in the first three lines of the problem doesn't explicitly acknowledge a link between republicans and nice. Thus we might have no a priori reason to include this link in the path diagram. However, the last line gives us very complete information about Dave, including the fact that he is Republican, which we would like to use.

The complete path diagram, including the link in question, looks like:

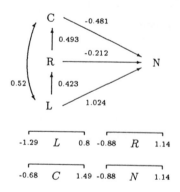

From this diagram it is possible, in the now-familiar way, to compute the probability that Dave is nice, given that he is at once a conservative, a Republican, and a lawyer. We have seen in previous examples how a path diagram may be collapsed to accommodate only partial information about the propositions which appear. Here we generalise this idea to partial reductions and, by reversing the argument, to expansions as well.

To generate the coefficients for the paths leading to N in the above diagram, the following equations were solved for the p's.

$$p_{ln} + p_m r_{rl} + p_{cn} r_{cl} = r_{ln}$$
$$p_{ln} r_{vx} + p_m + p_{cn} r_{cr} = r_m$$
$$p_{ln} r_{vy} + p_m r_{rc} + p_{cn} = r_{cn}$$

The r's are correlations between the subscripted variables. Had we known only that Dave was a conservative lawyer, that is, had we only known values for l and c, the centre arc from L to N would need to be eliminated. Here the usual collapsing technique won't work; the effect of the link from L to N through R can't simply be added to the direct link from L to N, because of the complicating link from R to C. Thus it is really necessary to compute a new path diagram. This is not difficult, however. The appropriate equations become

$$p'_{ln} + p'_{cn} r_{cl} = r_{ln}$$
$$p'_{ln} r_{lc} + p'_{cn} = r_{cn},$$

and their solution results in the following diagram:

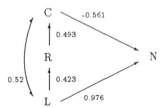

From these sets of equations, it can be seen that the correlations between the variables appearing in the diagram are the essential ingredients for generating the path coefficients. This suggests that the 'data structure' for encoding the available probabilistic knowledge consist of known correlations and the most complete path diagram which can be supported on causal grounds. Given little information, reduced diagrams can be computed by solving sets of simultaneous equations, and as more information became available, extended diagrams can be computed.

7   DISCUSSION

While we have not analysed all of the benchmark problems, enough of them have been examined in detail to give an indication of the power and flexibility of the path analytic approach. The solutions to many others have been obtained, but are not presented here because they demonstrate no new features of interest.

Many of the benchmark problems, when analysed using network-based models, exhibit loops (undirected cycles). The advantage of path analysis, as opposed to some other probabilistic methods, is that such loops are capably handled by the decomposition of influence. This is really the backbone of the method. For example, in Garfield and People, the loop was handled by collapsing the diagram. In this case, the only information given, after the construction of the graph, was that Garfield is a cat. In University Students, on the other hand, Fred is both a university student and an adult. Both these pieces of information are thus fixed; previous knowledge concerning the adultness of university students is irrelevant here, so the variables Adult and University Student are simply instantiated.

Default assumptions are recorded in the path diagram in an especially simple way. In the absence of additional information, either in the form of direct knowledge about a proposition or as a belief propagated from causal factors, the probability of a proposition is just its mean value. This represents its prior probability, which may subsequently be modified by additional information. In the path diagram, priors are recorded as zero values, since each variable is standardised before constructing the diagram. Thus if no additional information about a proposition is known, the corresponding variable is simply ignored – its default value is already embedded in the diagram as a whole.

The case of directed cycles is still a difficult problem. The standard example of 'seeing smoke makes fire more likely' and 'fire makes smoke more likely' illustrates how even a small belief in either smoke or fire can iteratively grow into compelling belief. There seems to be no satisfactory account of this problem in the literature, and path analysis, to the extent that we understand it, seems similarly unable to approach it. Wright [Wright 1960] gives a technique for handling a type of reciprocal interaction, but it appears to result in an infinite graph. Stochastic simulation techniques [Pearl 1988] could possibly be used, but what is really hoped for is a technique which stays within the path analytic framework. We have some reason to believe that tools from fixed point theory will help here, but the issue is far from resolved.

REFERENCES

Buchanan, B.G. and Shortliffe, E.H. (eds.) (1984) Rule-based Expert Systems: The MYCIN Experiments of the Stanford Heuristic Programming Project, Addison-Wesley Publishing Company, Reading, MA.

Cheeseman, P.C. (1983) A method for computing generalised Bayesian probability values for expert systems, Proceedings 8th International Joint Conference on Artificial Intelligence, Karlsruhe, Germany, pp. 198–202.

Gale, W.A. (ed.) (1986) Artificial Intelligence and Statistics, Addison-Wesley Publishing Company, Reading, MA.

Genesereth, M.R. and Nilsson, N.J. (1988) Logical Foundations of Artificial Intelligence, Morgan Kaufmann, Palo Alto, CA.

Glymour, C., Scheines, R., Spirtes, P. and Kelly, K. (1987) Discovering Causal Structure: Artificial Intelligence, Philosophy of Science, and Statistical Modeling, Academic Press, Inc., Harcourt Brace Jovanovich, Orlando, FL.

Harman, G. (1986) Change in View: Principles of Reasoning, The MIT Press, Cambridge, MA.

Kahneman, D., Slovic, P. and Tversky, A. (eds.) (1982) Judgement under Uncertainty: Heuristics and Biases, Cambridge University Press, Cambridge.

Kanal, L.N. and Lemmer, J.F. (1986) Uncertainty in Artificial Intelligence, North-Holland Publishing Company, New York.

Kimbrough, S.O. (1986) A graph representation for management of logic models, Decision Support Systems, 2, 27–37.

Kimbrough, S.O. (1991) An Introduction to the Method of Sweeping Presumptions for Modeling Nonmonotonic Reasoning, in J.F. Nunamaker, Jr., (ed.), Proceedings of the Twenty-Fourth Annual Hawaii International Conference on System Sciences, Vol. III, DSS and Knowledge-Based Systems and Collaboration Technology Tracks, Los Alamitos, CA: IEEE Computer Society Press, pp. 339–348.

Kimbrough, S.O. and Roehrig, S.F. (1990) On the path to practical probabilistic reasoning, Working Paper 90-02-03, Department of Decision Sciences, The Wharton School, University of Pennsylvania, Philadelphia, PA.

Li, C.C. (1977) Path Analysis – A Primer, The Boxwood Press, Pacific Grove, CA.

Loui, R. (1989) Benchmark problems for nonmonotonic systems, distributed at the Workshop on Defeasible Reasoning with Specificity and Multiple Inheritance, St Louis, MO, 7-9, April.

Murtagh, B.A. and Saunders, M.A. (1987) MINOS 5.1 User's Guide, Report SOL 83-20R, December 1983, revised January 1987, Stanford University.

Pearl, J. (1988) Probabilistic Reasoning in Intelligent Systems: Networks of Plausible Inference, Morgan Kaufmann Publishers, Inc., San Mateo, CA.

Shafer, G. and Pearl, J. (eds.) (1990) Readings in Uncertain Reasoning, Morgan Kaufmann Publishers, Inc., San Mateo, CA.

Smithson, M. (1989) Ignorance and Uncertainty: Emerging Paradigms, Springer-Verlag, New York, USA.

Wright, S. (1934) The method of path coefficients, Annals of Mathematical Statistics, 5, 161–215.

Wright, S. (1960) The treatment of reciprocal interaction, with or without lag, in path analysis, Biometrics, 16, 423–445.

12 On the path to practical probabilistic reasoning

S. O. Kimbrough* and S. F. Roehrig+
*The Wharton School, University of Pennsylvania
+The Heinz School, Carnegie Mellon University

1 INTRODUCTION

When reasoning, reasoning in the presence of uncertainty is the normal case. Given the scientific and practical importance of having a sound computational theory of reasoning, it is hardly surprising that a great deal of attention has been brought to bear on computational approaches to reasoning with uncertainty. We emphasise 'computational' because there is a broad, though not universal, agreement regarding what the theoretical approach should be to reasoning in the face of uncertainty. In principle, one's reasoning in the presence of uncertainty ought to conform to the mathematical theory of probability. It is widely recognised, however, that it is simply not possible to put the pure theory into practice. Computational limitations forbid this. While many approaches have been proposed for computationally sound techniques for reasoning in the face of uncertainty, the problem remains an open one.

Broadly speaking, three sorts of approaches have been proposed. Logicists have focused on qualitative, non-numerical techniques, and have typically (but not universally) aimed at developing some form of non-standard logic for reasoning with uncertainty. We shall have essentially nothing further to say about this approach here. Neo-calculists have taken the approach of using numerical representations for uncertainty, but based on calculi other than probability theory. Quite a number of such calculi have been proposed. In what follows, we will use the best known of these calculi, certainty factors, as a foil for the approach which is the main subject of this paper. Finally, neo-probabilists seek to use classical probability theory as much as possible for reasoning with uncertainty. The general strategy for neo-probabilists has been to find ways to import additional assumptions and representations which, in conjunction with standard probability theory, allow calculations and reasoning to proceed in practical situations.

At least for present purposes we are neo-probabilists. Our aim in this paper is to present and discuss a particular (neo-probabilist) computational approach to reasoning with uncertainty. The approach we favour is called extended path analysis. Remarkably, the theory of path analysis is drawn entirely from two statistical techniques that are broadly familiar to researchers in information systems and management science: least squares multiple regression and causal modelling. No arcane calculi need be mastered. Also remarkable is the fact that path analysis is an old (and well-established) technique, having been developed originally by the geneticist Sewall Wright during the years 1918-1921. What is new here is the application and interpretation of path analysis for reasoning in the face of uncertainty.

   We begin our exposition with a very brief discussion of the certainty factors approach to reasoning with uncertainty.

2   CERTAINTY FACTORS

Certainty factors, developed as part of the MYCIN project, are a kind of measure of belief on a scale extending from -1 (total disbelief) to $+1$ (total belief). Propositions, along with the rules that connect them, are endowed with certainty factors. There are a number of formulas for propagating beliefs in directed graphs [21], usage of these formulas being dictated by the logical structure of relationships between the propositions. As an example, suppose there are two rules $X \to Z$ (CF1) and $Y \to Z$ (CF2), where e.g. CF1 represents the certainty factor associated with the rule linking X and Z. Let x stand for the 'attenuated' belief in X, that is, the CF for X itself (call it CF_X), multiplies by the CF for the rule $X \to Z$ (CF1). Define y similarly. Then $z = CF_Z$, the CF for the proposition Z, is given by the ad hoc rule.

$$z = x \oplus y = \begin{cases} x + y - xy & x, y \geq 0 \\ (x + y) / (1 - \min(|x|, |y|)) & x, y \text{ opp. signs} \\ x + y + xy & x, y < 0 \end{cases}$$

   This rule of combination is in general continuous and monotone (but see below), which is often the intuitively correct behaviour. For instance, each of 'the car won't start' and 'the headlights are very dim' individually suggests a weak battery, and when taken together are an even stronger indication of the battery's demise. The two pieces of evidence support one another in this case, and this mutual support is reflected, at least qualitatively, in the certainty factors rule of combination.

   However, in some simple and frequently occurring circumstances, monotonicity makes it impossible to express the correct pattern of combination of evidence. (Here of course we use monotonicity in the mathematical sense of a monotone increasing or decreasing function, rather than in the logical sense of a monotonic or non-monotonic logic. There is clearly a direct relationship between the two.)

Consider the following example, dubbed "the kosher meal problem". Guests at an International House dinner try to guess the type of meal to be served, from among the possibilities of French, Chinese, vegetarian Indian, and kosher Israeli. Initially, with no hard evidence with which to work, belief in any particular meal might be roughly the same for all. Upon receipt of the clue "the meal contains meat", the consensus belief in the Indian meal drops precipitously, leaving the total belief to be divided up between the remaining three, a net increase for each. Alternatively, had the clue been "the meal contains milk", a similar reaction would occur, this time comprising a decrease in belief that the Chinese meal will be served, and a corresponding increase in belief that the others might be. Receipt of either of these clues alone thus prompts greater belief that a kosher meal might appear on the table. However, both clues together, given either simultaneously or in any order, preclude the possibility of such a meal. Any monotone rule of combination of belief, certainty factors included, is therefore incapable of dealing with this situation.

In the case where CF1 = 1 and CF2 = 1, the certainty factors rule of combination is again continuous on the interior of the square, x, y $\in$ [–1,1], but exhibits a somewhat strange behaviour on the boundary. Essentially, it is required that the surface z = x $\oplus$ y meet the bold edges in the following drawing.

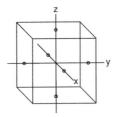

A jump discontinuity in belief in Z occurs at points where one supporting proposition is totally believed while the other is totally disbelieved. For example, if X is totally disbelieved (CF_x = –1) while Y is strongly, but not totally, believed (say CF_y = 0.95), then Z is totally disbelieved. On the other hand, CF_x = –0.95 and CF_y = 1 yields total belief in Z. The certainty factors rule of combination thus demands, in this context, that a rule such as X $\rightarrow$ Z also entails ¬X $\rightarrow$ ¬Z, so that the rule is essentially a biconditional.

This very brief look at certainty factors might seem rather harsh, in light of the fact that some systems employing them have been quite successful. Our aim, however, is to show that another approach, based on path analysis, can overcome the expressive limitations of certainty factors (and other systems as well), while maintaining the intuitive appeal sought by its developers.

3   PATH ANALYSIS BASICS

Path analysis is a method of "decomposing and interpreting linear relationships among a set of variables by assuming that (1) a (weak) casual order among these variables is known and (2) the relationships among these variables are casually closed". Although "primarily a method of working out the logical consequences" of these two assumptions, the structure and associated numerical assignments of path diagrams possess, at a superficial level, a similarity to some of the diagrams and techniques currently being used as belief calculi in the AI community. We will show in section 4 that there is in fact a deeper connection, but here our goal is simply – and very briefly – to explicate and illustrate the method.

Briefly, path analysis begins with a causal model for the modelling variables at hand. We may think of a causal model as a directed graph, with modelling variables at nodes and causal influences represented by arcs. For a given causal model, variables (nodes) with no incoming directed arcs are exogenous. All other variables are endogenous. Correlations between pairs of exogenous variables are indicated by bi-directional arcs between the corresponding nodes. In addition, path analysis requires formal completeness, or causal closure, for the endogenous variables in its causal models. In the event that an endogenous variable, call it z, is not completely determined by the variables residing at the sources of its incoming arcs, then a new exogenous variable, call it u, is added to the causal model and an arc drawn from it to the z node. No other arcs, either directed or bi-directional, are attached to u. The idea is that u represents all other causes of z and that these causes, whatever they are, are assumed to be uncorrelated with the exogenous variables of the causal model.

Given a proper causal model for a set of variables and corresponding observations on the variables, the theory of path analysis provides for calculating labels on the arcs in the causal model. Directed arcs are labelled with path coefficients, which may be found by least squares regression, as described below. Bi-directional arcs are labelled with the sample correlation coefficients between the exogenous variables in question. Labelled in this way, a causal model is said to be a path diagram, which may then be interpreted to indicate numerically the causal strengths and means of influence (direct or indirect) for the model's variables, assuming that the causal model is qualitatively correct. How this interpretation proceeds is beyond the scope of this paper. We refer the reader to the references on path analysis, cited below.

We shall now illustrate these points about path analysis with a simple example. We assume only a basic understanding of regression and correlation, but much of what is said can be understood on an intuitive level.

3.1   Example

Suppose we have available to us a set of data consisting of measurements of three related variables, x, y and z. For concreteness, we might assume that the variables represent the area (in square metres), condition (on a scale of 1 to 20), and selling price (in hundreds of dollars) of Persian rugs from a particular region. Depending on our point of view, there are a number of ways we might look at the relationships between the variables. An appraiser trying to determine the approximate value of a given rug might think of the size and condition of the rug as predictors or 'causes' of the selling price. Alternatively, someone reading a newspaper advertisement might try to gauge the condition of a rug from the announced area and selling price.

Any analysis of the data using path analysis requires first of all that a causal model be assumed. While the correlations between variables remain the same regardless of the ordering, the results of path analysis can only be interpreted in connection with a path diagram representing the assumed order. For the first interpretation above, the path diagram looks like the one on the left below, while for the second interpretation, the diagram on the right is implied.

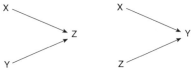

Focusing on the first of these two interpretations, we need to fulfil the remaining assumption of path analysis – causal closure. It is unreasonable to suppose that the selling price of a rug will depend only on its size and condition; what other factors remain, if left unspecified, must be subsumed by another variable, say U, which we take to be uncorrelated with both size and condition. In addition, there may or may not be a correlation between X and Y; provision should be made for correlation in the path diagram, even if it seems clear a priori that X and Y are independent. The resulting, complete path diagram is then

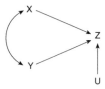

where the curved double-headed arrow indicates the correlation. There is no such arrow joining U with either X or Y, since these are assumed uncorrelated.

Path analysis is based on least squares, multilinear regression. Each variable in the causal model with incoming arcs is regressed onto the variables at the sources of those arcs. While it is by no means necessary, it is useful to work with standardised variables, that is, variables transformed from the originals so as to have zero means and unit standard deviations. If we take the first interpretation above, and thus adopt the causally closed diagram to represent our assumptions, the variable U represents the residuals of the regression of Z onto X and Y.

We now present some (fictitious) raw data, the same data in standardised form (denoted by upper case letters), and some terms used in the regression analysis. In what follows, we adopt notation from the path analysis literature; 0 stands for the regressed variable – here Z – while 1, 2 ... denote the predictors. For example, p_{01} is the path coefficient from X to Z, while r_{12} is the correlation between X and Y.

	x	y	z	X	Y	Z
	10	3	8	-1.25	-1.40	-1.08
	9	5	4	-1.50	-1.00	-1.24
	20	6	21	1.25	-0.80	-0.56
	17	8	49	0.50	-0.40	0.56
	11	11	26	-1.00	0.20	-0.36
	18	14	33	0.75	0.80	-0.08
	18	15	84	0.75	1.00	1.97
	18	18	55	0.50	1.60	0.80
Mean	15	10	35	0.00	0.00	0.00
σ	4	5	24.9	1.00	1.00	1.00

	$\hat{Z}$	U	X^2	Y^2	XY	XZ	YZ
	-1.24	0.16	1.56	1.96	1.75	1.35	1.51
	-1.08	-0.16	2.25	1.00	1.50	1.86	1.24
	-0.08	-0.48	1.56	0.64	1.00	-0.70	0.45
	-0.08	0.64	0.25	0.16	0.20	0.28	-0.20
	-0.20	-0.16	1.00	0.04	0.20	0.36	-0.07
	0.72	-0.80	0.56	0.64	0.60	-0.06	-0.06
	0.84	1.12	0.56	1.00	0.75	1.48	1.97
	1.12	-0.32	0.25	2.56	0.80	0.40	1.28
Mean	0.00	0.00	1.00	1.00	0.50	0.62	0.76
σ	0.81	0.58			r_{21}	r_{01}	r_{02}

Because the variables have been standardised, the linear regression of Z onto X and Y has no constant term. The appropriate normal equations are

$$p_{01} \sum X^2 + p_{02} \sum XY = \sum XZ$$

$$p_{01} \sum XY + p_{02} \sum Y^2 = \sum YZ$$

When solved for the so-called path coefficients p_{01} and p_{02} we find $p_{01} = 0.32$ and $p_{02} = 0.60$ so that

$$\hat{Z} = p_{01}X + p_{02}Y = 0.32X + 0.60Y$$

The multiple correlation between Z and its 'causes' X and Y is defined to be the simple correlation between Z and $\hat{Z}$,

$$R_{0(12)} = R(Z,\hat{Z}) = \frac{\text{Cov}(Z,\hat{Z})}{\sigma_Z \, \sigma_{\hat{Z}}} = 0.81$$

and the total variance of Z is the sum of the variances of its uncorrelated components

$$\sigma_Z^2 = \sigma_{\hat{Z}}^2 + \sigma_U^2 = 1$$

Thus the path coefficient for the path $U \rightarrow Z$ is, because of the standardisation, just the standard deviation of U:

$$\sigma_U = r_{0U} = 0.58$$

Thus the completed path diagram looks like the following.

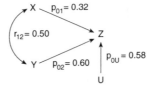

3.2   Interpretation of the Path Diagram

First of all, it is clear how predicted values for the variable z are obtained. Given values for x and y, it is merely necessary to standardise, substitute into the regression equation (using the path coefficients) and convert back to an unstandardised result. But what if only, say, x is known? It turns out that the path diagram summarises all the information needed to recover the (standardised) regression of Z onto X alone.

For the case of a single causal variable X → Z, that is, ignoring the contribution of Y, the path coefficient is in fact equal to the correlation coefficient, and we may write

$$r_{01} = p_{01} + p_{02}r_{21}$$

This corresponds (graphically) to navigation two routes from Z through X and back to Z. The first is the more direct: Z to X and back to Z. The second is the round trip from Z to X, through Y, and back to Z. The effect of the correlation of X and Y is captured by the term $p_{02}r_{21}$. The correlation between Z and X has been decomposed into two components, each corresponding to a connecting path.

The degree of determination of Z by a set of variables is the proportion of the variance of Z accounted for by those variables. The degree of determination of Z by $\hat{Z}$ is given by

$$\sigma_{\hat{Z}}^2 = E\,(p_{01}X + p_{02}Y)^2$$

$$= p_{01}^2 + p_{02}^2 + p_{01}r_{12}p_{02} + p_{02}r_{21}p_{01}$$

The four terms in this equation correspond to the four round trips which may be traversed from Z back to itself, that is, Z → X → Z, Z → Y → Z, Z → X → Y → Z, and Z → Y → X → Z. These terms, plus the unique round trip Z → U → Z, which yields the degree of determination of Z by U, together sum to 1, as expected.

To summarise, path analysis provides the means to decompose the correlations between causal variables. While the example presented here involves only two causal variables, the extension to greater numbers is straightforward; in every case the path diagram provides all the necessary information. Similarly, path analytic techniques exist for situations in which a given variable directly influences several others. In fact, any causal ordering which can be represented as an acyclic graph is amenable to path analysis.

Finally, the method insists on the causal closure of the path diagram, and gives an indication, by way of residuals uncorrelated with the explicit variables, of the cogency of the causal explanation of the system under investigation.

4   PATH ANALYSIS: A PROBABILISTIC INTERPRETATION

It may seem at this point that path analysis, a statistical procedure, has little to say concerning the degree of certainty one should attach to propositions which may be either true or false. Certainty factors, as we have seen, deal directly with beliefs associated with propositions, but have somewhat limited expressive power and lack a clear operational interpretation. Probability, on the other hand, has a clear interpretation in terms of frequency of occurrence, or from the subjectivist point of view, scoring rules [9]. We show here that path analysis, when applied to data on propositional variables, gives results that are in complete agreement with those obtained from probability theory.

Again, it is useful to work with some concrete data. Suppose now that x, y and z are propositional variables, and we have the following data concerning their joint occurrence:

x	y	z
1	1	1
1	0	1
0	1	1
0	1	1
0	1	0
1	1	1
1	0	0
0	0	0
1	1	1
1	0	0

Now, from the point of view of a probabilist, this data may be summarised by a joint probability distribution, or perhaps more succinctly as marginal and conditional probabilities. The degree of summarisation depends on what the data will be used for – the appropriate data structure will reflect any additional assumptions made. If, for example, it is assumed that x and y are independent 'causes' of z (so that positive belief in x or y (or both) change the a priori belief in z), then the data can be summarised in terms of the conditionals $P(z \mid x)$ and $P(z \mid y)$.

Path analysis also performs a summarising function. Under the causal assumptions given above, standardised regression results in the following diagram.

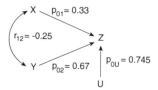

Note that although we assume that x and y are independent, the correlation from the data is non-zero. This is just an artefact of sampling. Once again, the individual influence of either x or y on z can be computed from the composite diagram. For instance, isolating x as the sole, explicitly identified, cause of z yields the following:

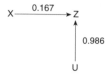

We will use this diagram as a starting point in relating path analysis to probability.

The regression equation implied by the diagram tells us that if we wish to 'predict' a belief in z, here written Bel(z), given some Bel(x), we should standardise Bel(x), multiply the path coefficient, and lastly unstandardise. For example, if Bel(x) = 1/2, we obtain Bel(z) = 7/12.

On the other hand, a probabilistic summary of the data tells us that

$$P(z \mid x) = 2/3 \text{ and } P(z \mid \neg x) = 1/2$$

and in general this is exactly the information that we would expect to be provided by statistical data or expert opinion. Now, we want to obtain a probability for z given partial belief in x. Since the conditional probability formalism requires that we know the truth or falsity of the conditioning variable with certainty, we resort to the ruse of a dummy variable x′. This variable expresses virtual evidence, we imagine some evidence x′ known with certainty which causes us to believe in x with a stated probability. Then

$$P(z \mid x') = P(z \mid x) \cdot P(x \mid x') + P(z \mid \neg x) \cdot P(\neg x \mid x')$$

Calculation gives P(z | x′) = 7/12, the same as the path diagram.

It is possible to re-write the belief update equation as

$$P(z \mid x') = [P(z \mid x) - P(z \mid \neg x)] p + P(z \mid \neg x)$$

where $p = P(x \mid x')$, which lays bare the linearity (in p). For a given p (that is, a given value of confidence in the evidence), the resulting belief in z is just the linear interpolation between $P(z \mid x)$ and $P(z \mid \neg x)$.

It is not hard to see why the probability procedure corresponds exactly to the result from path analysis. All the data points, when graphed, lie on the extreme points of the unit square (unit hypercube in higher dimensions), so that, at least in the case of a single predictor variable, the (unstandardised) regression line is easily characterised. The figure below shows the unit square, along with the numbers of data points at each corner. It is clear that to minimise the sum of squares deviation of the regression line and the data, points should be chosen at (0, 1/2) and (1, 2/3) and the regression line taken to join them. For any value of x we simply interpolate along this line. The standardised path regression is just a linear transformation of this.

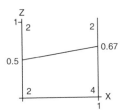

To analyse the case where two variables x and y influence the variable z, we use all the data in the table above, and the path diagram resulting from it. We assume (for now) that x and y are independent, and again suppose that two dummy variables x' and y' represent events known with certainty, which give rise to belief in x and y with given probabilities. We also assume that $P(y \mid x', y') = P(y \mid y')$.

One way to compute the updated belief in z given evidence concerning x and y is as follows. Because of the independence assumptions, it is possible to write

$$P(z \mid x', y') = P(z \mid y, x') P(y \mid y') + P(z \mid \neg y, x') P(\neg y \mid y')$$

which again can be seen as a linear interpolation between $P(z \mid y, x')$ and $P(z \mid \neg y, x')$, weighted by the probability of y. The term $P(z \mid y, x')$ can be determined from

$$O(z \mid y, x') = \frac{P(y \mid z, x')}{P(y \mid \neg z, x')} O(z \mid x')$$

$$= \frac{P(y \mid z)}{P(y \mid \neg z)} O(z \mid x')$$

where $O(z \mid x')$ are the odds on z which resulted from an update information on x alone. Thus this is a sequential update scheme, and we would expect (and, in fact, get) that the process is symmetric with respect to the order of updating.

The graphical interpretation of the two-variable case is as follows.

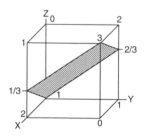

Again the number of data points associated with each corner is recorded, and it is easy to check that the plane drawn in is the appropriate regression.

The term $P(x \mid \neg y, x')$ represents a point on the line segment joining (0,0,0) and (1,0,1/3) in (x, y, z) space, that is, the probability of z given that y = 0 and the previously assimilated information about x. We know this because

$$P(z \mid \neg y, x') = P(z \mid \neg y, x) P(x \mid x') + P(z \mid \neg y, \neg x) P(\neg x \mid x')$$

and $(P(z \mid \neg y, x)$ and $P(z \mid \neg y, x)$ correspond to the points (0,0,0) and (1,0,1/3). A similar remark applies to $P(z \mid y, x')$. Now, since $P(z \mid x', y')$ is gotten by interpolating between these two points, the surface of possible triples (x,y,z) obtainable from the probability formula must lie on the regression plane. Thus in the two-dimensional case (and, by analogy, in higher dimensions) the path analysis and the probability procedure agree.

In the foregoing analysis it was assumed that x and y were independent, and furthermore that they were conditionally independent given the value of z. The conditional independence assumption is many times unwarranted, and the inability of many belief calculi (e.g. certainty factors) to relax this assumption is a drawback that path analysis can overcome. Here we analyse a simple example involving conditional dependence (adapted from an example of Pearl [21]), and then show how the same technique can be used to deal with the kosher meal problem.

Suppose two coins are flipped independently, and a bell sounds if the coins come up either both heads or both tails. Let x (resp. y) stand for the proposition that coin 1 (resp. 2) come up heads, and let x represent the proposition that the bell is ringing. Clearly, the outcomes of the two coins are not independent if we know the state of the bell – if the first coin is heads and the bell is ringing, we know the state of the second coin. Probabilistically, we can write

$$P(z) = P(x)\,P(y) + P(\neg x)\,P(\neg y)$$
$$= 1 + 2P(x)\,P(y) - (P(x) + P(y))$$

where the last line makes explicit the interaction of the coin outcomes.

To model this situation using regression, it is necessary to incorporate an interaction term in the regression equation, and add a node corresponding to this term to the path diagram. In what follows, we leave the variables unstandardised to facilitate comparison between the probabilistic analysis and regression. Imagining the coins and bell scenario to be repeated a large number of times, we end up with a data set consisting of equal numbers of the four points (x, y, z), $(x, \neg y, \neg z)$, $(\neg x, y, \neg z)$ and $(\neg x, \neg y, z)$. To facilitate numerical calculations, set $x = 1$ if coin 1 comes up heads, 0 if tails, and do the same for y. Finally, take $z = 1$ if the bell rings and $z = 0$ if not. Then regression on the 'data points' yields the equation.

$$z = 1 + 2xy - (x + y)$$

which is again identical with the probability result. Thus for any degree of belief in the two coins coming up heads, we can calculate the appropriate belief in the bell's ringing.

It is now possible to see how to handle the problem at the International House. Assume that, in the absence of any further information, the belief that the kosher meal will be served is 1/4, and that after either (but not both) of the two clues, it is 1/3. Taking x as the proposition "the meal is kosher", let x and y be the propositions "we received the clue that the meal contains meat" and "we received the clue that the meal contains milk". Note that, e.g. x is not "the meal contains meat", since the negation of this is "the meal does not contain meat", a statement we would have no right making in the absence of the clue.

The information to hand concerning the joint probability distribution for x, y, and z is

$$P(z) \quad\;\; = 1/4$$
$$P(z \mid x) \;\; = 1/3$$
$$P(z \mid y) \;\; = 1/3$$
$$P(z \mid x,y) = 0$$

The distribution has $2^3 = 8$ entries, and we have the above four constraints, plus the usual sums-to-one constraint. Thus, in the absence of base rate information on the probabilities of receiving the clues, a probabilistic analysis is underconstrained. One way to impute a probability distribution which agrees with all the known data, and which introduces no new information (in the information-theoretic sense), is the method of maximum entropy [7]. Without going into detail, this amounts to computing the distribution P_{xyz} which maximises the entropy function

$$H = -\sum_{xyz} P_{xyz} \log P_{xyz}$$

where the sum is taken over all values in the joint distribution.

For the kosher meal problem, the application of this maximisation results in the following distribution.

$$P_{000} = \frac{16}{44} \quad P_{100} = \frac{7}{44} \quad P_{010} = \frac{7}{44} \quad P_{001} = \frac{1}{44}$$

$$P_{110} = \frac{3}{44} \quad P_{101} = \frac{5}{44} \quad P_{011} = \frac{5}{44} \quad P_{111} = 0$$

When we fit a multiplicative regression model onto the distribution, we get an exact fit; the regression equation looks like

$$z = 0.0588 + 0.3578(x + y) - 0.7745xy$$

This equation alone is not, however, sufficient to extract the unconditional belief in z, that is, $P(z) = 1/4$. In fact, when x and y are equal, a condition which presumably must obtain whenever we don't explicitly consider the evidence they represent, the maximum value of x is 0.224. (We shall see later that we need to take z, y and xy at their mean values – this is the only way to properly recover the unconditional belief in z, that is, its mean value.) So the regression itself matches only the path diagram which, by its structure, presupposes some definite belief in x and y. This is nothing new – the identical situation exists in the purely linear case. What is needed is a way to 'collapse' the path diagram, in a way similar to the linear case.

The method of path coefficients provides just such a way. If we imagine many "trials" of the International House situation, in which the two clues come to us with the frequencies specified by the fitted distribution, we can standardise the "data" in the usual way, and fit a regression equation to the standardised variables. A path diagram, incorporating every possible arc looks like

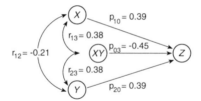

The standardised X and Y variables fall on a scale of [−0.719, 1.39], (corresponding to x, y ∈ [0,1]), XY is in [−0.271, 3.70], and Z is in [0.577, 1.73]. Now we see that by taking X, Y and XY at the standardised values of zero, corresponding to the mean values of x, y, and xy, we can arrive at the true unconditional belief in z, which is just $Z = 0$ (or $P(z) = 1/4$). Further, it is easy to calculate the value of Z conditioned on, say, X alone: there are three paths from X to Z in the diagram, the situation is identical to that of three linear predictors. We have

$$r_{01} = p_{01} + r_{12}p_{02} + r_{13}p_{30} = 0.13838$$

Given any (standardised) belief X in x, the simple path diagram

$$X \xrightarrow{r_{10} = 0.14} Z$$

enables us to compute the belief in z, in the absence of any knowledge of y, that is P(z | x).

These ideas can clearly be extended to more than two 'clues' or items of evidence. Of course, the regression equation becomes more cumbersome, but so will the rule of combination for any reasonable belief calculus. The point is that the regression approach is entirely general – virtually any smooth combination function can be approximated as closely as desired, if not exactly achieved.

5   CRITERIA FOR PROBABILISTIC REASONING

So far we have presented the problem of reasoning with uncertainty (section 1); given a brief description of certainty factors, the currently most popular numerical approach to reasoning with uncertainty, at least in expert systems (section 2); presented the basics of path analysis (section 3); and shown how path analysis can be used as a proper probabilistic representation for reasoning with uncertainty (section 4). Thus, we have shown how certainty factors and path analysis are competing approaches to reasoning with uncertainty. The question naturally arises which approach is better and under what conditions.

Our aim in the present section is to begin discussion of the larger issue of comparing path analysis to all other approaches to reasoning with uncertainty. Completion of that discussion is well beyond the scope of this paper. Our aims here are quite limited. In the present section we propose several desiderata for any system of reasoning with uncertainty, and we present a brief evaluation of certainty factors and path analysis. Superiority of one method or another, even in a specific context, is not something that can be proved in the absence of agreed upon principles for comparison. Nor are the principles themselves proper objects for proof. All we can say – both in general and specifically in what follows – is that particular principles appear, reasonable and reasonably complete, and that those who disagree are burdened with producing exceptions.

5.1   Any method for reasoning with uncertainty should be probabilistically correct, given the assumptions it makes

This is a fairly weak constraint in the sense that the behaviour of nearly any method can be justified on the basis of some probabilistic assumptions. Many methods, however, are employed without regard to whether their probabilistic assumptions apply or not. In such cases, the methods are dubbed heuristics and often little or no attempt is made to validate the assumptions of a given method. One simply attempts to make it work with the application at hand. If reasonable success is achieved, the heuristic is judged apt. This is the typical situation when certainty factors are employed with expert systems. No doubt such practice can at times be justified. If the resulting software works well, one shouldn't gainsay it. Nevertheless, it can hardly be denied that it is highly desirable, for any given method for reasoning with uncertainty, that it be known what assumptions the method makes and how robust the method is under violations of these assumptions.

The conditions under which certainty factors are probabilistically correct have been explored and turn out to be rather limited. Some of these limitations were demonstrated above in our discussion of how certainty factors cannot handle the kosher meal problem and, generally, cases in which factors interact and enter into the model multiplicatively. Little is known about the robustness of certainty factors under violations of assumptions of probabilistic correctness.

The upshot of section 4 was to demonstrate that for any relationship among variables representable in an acyclic path diagram (and this is a very broad class of relationship), path analysis agrees with probability theory. In particular, dependence among exogenous variables is easily accommodated and is represented by correlation arcs. Also, as we have shown in the kosher meal example, multiplicative effects, e.g. $x \cdot y$, are easily and naturally handled with path analytic techniques. That the point generalises can be seen by noting that path analysis works from a causal model and a linear regression model:

$$Z = p_1 \cdot X_1 + \ldots + p_n \cdot X_n \qquad (1)$$

The linear model is linear in the parameters, that is the p_i terms (or the a_i when concrete, rather than path, coefficients are estimated). The X_i may be related to one another in any manner so long as it does not functionally involve the p_i terms. Thus $X_i \cdot X_j$ is just a special case. With Taylor expansions, the linear model can be used to estimate nearly any functional relation among the X_i factors. In sum, the expressive powers of path analysis and of causal models are quite remarkable and, given the assumptions behind any given causal model, the match with probability theory is exact.

5.2 Any method for reasoning with uncertainty should be visible with respect to its assumptions

This is a more subtle requirement than the first. The basic idea here is that any method for reasoning with uncertainty will have a corresponding way of representing uncertain knowledge. Given a representation in a particular case, ideally it should be easy to see what assumptions are being made, and given a particular set of assumptions, it should be easy to see what the particular representation should be.

The contrast in this regard between certainty factors and path analysis is especially sharp. Given a labelled path diagram it is entirely transparent which variables are assumed to be independent and which are not, what the causal relations among the variables are, and what the observed correlations among the variables should be. Moreover, the path diagram allows one to determine by inspection which variables are endogenous and which are exogenous. Certainty factors, on the other hand, can be represented graphically in a meaningful way only in the special case in which the assumptions of probabilistic correctness obtain, in which case the graph would coincide with that for a path analysis.

Neither method is especially strong at producing a representation from a given set of assumptions. In the case of path analysis, it is clear that a given data set on n variables is formally consistent with 2^{n^2-n} causal models (and more if presence of correlations among exogenous variables is taken into account).[1] With both methods, the work of constructing a particular model only begins when the assumptions are given.

5.3   Any method for reasoning with uncertainty should be expressively powerful; it should be able to handle in a natural way a rich variety of relationships among the factors it represents

Another way of putting this point is that it is desirable that a method for reasoning with uncertainty be complete in the sense that it can accommodate all available information. When a representation method is not sufficiently rich, the model builder is forced to fit the problem to the technique, which becomes something of a Procrustean bed.

Our earlier remarks, in sections 4 and 5.1, suffice to illustrate the virtues of path analysis and the vices of certainty factors in this regard.

5.4   Any method for reasoning with uncertainty should be able to accommodate both new data and structural changes in a computationally easy manner

A closely related requirement, something of a sub-requirement, is that the representation method permit simplifying assumptions to be explored easily.

Again, certainty factors come off a poor second choice to path analysis. Given a causal model and new data, it is a simple matter to recalculate the path coefficients and the correlations among the exogenous variables. The analog of new data in the case of certainty factors would be an additional judgement regarding the relations among the variables at hand. Incorporating

---

1   Given any two variables, X and Y, there are four possible direct causal relationships: X causally influences Y, but Y does not causally influence X and vice versa, Z and Y are mutually causally influential, and X and Y have no direct causal connection. Thus there are four causal models for every two variables. In a system with n variables there will be $4^{c(n,2)} = 2^{n^2-n}$ causal models, where $c(n,2) = n!/(n-2)!\cdot 2!$. Path analysis does not countenance all possible causal models. Even so, the fact remains that the number of causal models to be considered in principle is 2^X, where X is $O(n^2)$. There are a lot of causal models to consider.

this information is a notoriously dicey proposition and extensive testing of the revised knowledge base is normally required (cf., the Teiresias system, described in [8]; the exchanges of memoranda during the MYCIN project, reported in [6]). Given an approximately correct causal model, it is fairly easy to add and remove terms (e.g. interaction terms) and to reorient causal arcs. Systematic exploration of alternative causal models is, however, a computationally demanding task [12], especially given the large number of alternative causal models (see above).

5.5   Any method for reasoning with uncertainty should be interpretable in a sensible way

When a method corresponds, under the given assumptions, with a probabilistic interpretation, it is a simple and uncontroversial matter to provide an interpretation of the resulting model. When a method – and especially a quantitative[1] method – departs from conformity with probability theory, then there is a heavy burden of proof on the claim that the method can be interpreted meaning- fully. We see no indication that this burden has been lifted in the case of certainty factors. The virtues of path analysis in this regard have been discussed above.

5.6   Any method for reasoning with uncertainty should have available diagnostics that can test the adequacy of a particular model using that method

Statistical models generally, with their goodness-of-fit tests, score well in this regard. The literature on regression diagnostics is particularly well developed. Path analysis inherits the benefits of this literature. There is no comparable theory in the case of certainty factors.

5.7   Any method for reasoning with uncertainty should provide both prediction and explanation

Simple regression analysis is notoriously a predictive technique, rather than an explanatory technique. Briefly, an explanation is an answer to a why-question

---

1   For certain qualitative techniques for reasoning with uncertainty, which may be classified as logicist approaches, it may be possible to provide a meaningful formal semantics. While this claim has not gone unchallenged, discussion of it here would take us too far afield.

and probably involves an appeal to causation. One may surely be able to predict something without being able to explain it. Knowing the forecast allows one to predict rain, but the forecast does not explain why it will rain.

When regression analysis is augmented with causal modelling (in particular path analysis), it can be used both to predict and to explain phenomena. This fact provides a main motivation for application of causal modelling techniques. Arguably, certainty factors may likewise have explanatory power. In the event that the probabilistic assumptions for certainty factors are satisfied, it would be hard to deny that explanations are possible. When the assumptions are not satisfied, however, it is difficult to see how any 'explanations' based on certainty factors can be interpreted. We leave this question for others.

At worst, then, it is safe to conclude that path analysis is not inferior to certainty factors in its ability to provide meaningful explanations.

5.8   Any method for reasoning with uncertainty should not display anomalous behaviour

We are aware of no such behaviour in the case of path analysis. Perversely mistaken causal models will, of course, yield weird path coefficients, but we view this as a virtue of path analysis: weirdness is a diagnostic, indicating a poorly-formed model. In section 2 we described a general case in which what should be an implication between two variables is forced by certainty factors to be a biconditional. For those willing to look, certainty factors can be made to yield a great abundance of anomalous behaviour.

6   CONCLUSION

The main contribution of this paper has been to show that – and to indicate how – path analysis may be employed as a probabilistically correct method for reasoning in the face of uncertainty (given the assumptions of the particular causal model at hand). We have also compared path analysis with certainty factors, the alternative technique most widely used in expert systems. In the comparison, path analysis comes off quite well.

Much remains to be done. Here is our shortlist.

1. Other graph-based techniques for reasoning with uncertainty need to be investigated and compared with path analysis. Pearl has done an excellent job of examining various such techniques. Although he mentions path analysis, he does not treat it. We believe that, on several of the criteria discussed in section 5, path analysis will prove superior to any of the

methods Pearl discusses in his work. That, however, is a subject for future papers, and much longer papers.

2. Certainty factors are easily incorporated into rule-based expert systems as presently architected. We have not addressed at all the pragmatics of using path analysis, i.e. of exploiting and manipulating a given causal model and data set. These pragmatics will inevitably be more complex than those associated with certainty factors, although not, we believe, much more complex than those required for other graph-based methods. In any case, the outstanding issues here are legion.

3. As noted above, there are a large number of possible causal models for a given collection of n variables. Happily, there are model diagnostics inherited from regression theory and it is also possible to import ancillary information in order to select and evaluate particular causal models. The possibilities here loom large, but are far from having been completely explored. Solid, if incomplete, work in this regard has begun, and we foresee ample research needs and opportunities in this direction.

4. We believe that the opportunities are manifold, both for behavioural and cognitive research and for innovative organisational applications, in connection with path analysis. Path diagrams are built upon causal models, which are qualitative, graph-based representations. As such, they are conceptually accessible to a very broad range of people. Further, in virtue of being graph-based, causal models lend themselves to salient display, supported by sophisticated computer processing. People and organisations find PERT diagrams, decision trees, network flow diagrams, flowcharts, data flow diagrams, and so on, useful, in part because these models are based on graph representations. Many different sorts of people are able to understand, to reason about, and to contribute to insightful exploitation of these graph-based models. It is, we think, not too much to hope that path analytic models may be added to the list. If so, then the manifest need for, and usefulness of, behavioural and cognitive research into how people think about graph-based models will only gain impetus from exploitation of path analytic models. We are pleased to note that behavioural research pertaining to graph-based models is beginning to appear in the MIS literature.

In sum, this paper is hardly the last word on the use of path analysis and causal modelling for reasoning with uncertainty. It is, however, an early word, and we think an auspicious one at that.

REFERENCES

[1] Adams, J.B. (1976) Probabilistic Reasoning and Certainty Factors, Mathematical Biosciences, 32, 177–186; reprinted with editing in [5].

[2] Belsley, D.A., Kuh, E. and Welsch, R.E. (1980) Regression Diagnostics: Identifying Influential Data and Sources of Collinearity, John Wiley & Sons, Inc., New York.

[3] Blalock, Hubert M., Jr. (1964) Causal Inferences in Nonexperimental Research, W.W. Norton & Company Inc., New York.

[4] Blalock, H.M, Jr. (ed.) (1985) Causal Models in the Social Sciences, 2nd ed. Aldine de Gruyter, Hawthorne, New York.

[5] Buchanan, B.G. and Shortliffe, E.H. (eds.) (1984) Rule-based Expert Systems: The MYCIN Experiments of the Stanford Heuristic Programming Project, Addison-Wesley Publishing Company, Reading, Massachusetts.

[6] Buchanan, B.G. and Shortliffe, E.H. (1984) Uncertainty and Evidential Support, in [5], 209–232.

[7] Cheeseman, P.C. (1983) A Method for Computing Generalised Bayesian Probability Values for Expert Systems, Proceedings 8th International Joint Conference on Artificial Intelligence, Karlsruhe, West Germany, pp. 198–202.

[8] Davis, R. and Lenat, D.B. (1982) Knowledge-based Systems in Artificial Intelligence, McGraw-Hill International Book Company, New York.

[9] De Finetti, B. (1972) Probability, Induction and Statistics, John Wiley & Sons, New York.

[10] Gale, W.A. (ed.) (1986) Artificial Intelligence and Statistics, Addison-Wesley Publishing Company, Reading, Massachusetts.

[11] Genesereth, M.R. and Nilsson, N.J. (1988) Logical Foundations of Artificial Intelligence, Morgan Kaufmann, Palo Alto, California.

[12] Glymour, C., Scheines, R., Spirtes, P. and Kelly, K. (1987) Discovering Causal Structure: Artificial Intelligence, Philosophy of Science, and Statistical Modelling, Academic Press Inc., Harcourt Brace Jovanovich, Orlando, Florida.

[13] Harman, G. (1986) Change in View: Principles of Reasoning, MIT Press, Cambridge, Massachusetts.

[14] Johnson, R.A. and Wichern, D.W. (1982) Applied Multivariate Statistical Analysis, Prentice-Hall Inc., Englewood Cliffs, New Jersey.

[15] Jones, C.V. (1988) An Introduction to Graph-based Modeling Systems, University of Pennsylvania, Department of Decision Sciences, working paper 88-10-02.

[16]Jones, C. (1990) An Example-based Introduction to Graph Grammars for Modeling, Proceedings of the Twenty-Third Annual Hawaii International Conference on System Sciences, Volume III, IEEE Computer Society Press, Los Alamitos, California, pp. 433–442.

[17]Kanal, L.N. and Lemmer, J.F. (1986) Uncertainty in Artificial Intelligence, North-Holland Publishing Company, New York.

[18]Kimbrough, S.O. and Adams, F. (1988) Why Nonmonotonic Logic? Decision Support Systems, 4, pp. 111–127.

[19]Li, C.C. (1977) Path Analysis – a Primer, The Boxwood Press, Pacific Grove, California.

[20]Pearl, J. (1987) Embracing Causality in Formal Reasoning, Proceedings of AAAI-87, Volume 1, Sixth International Conference on Artificial Intelligence, Morgan Kaufmann Publishers, Los Altos, California, pp. 369–373.

[21]Pearl, J. (1988) Probabilistic Reasoning in Intelligent Systems: Networks of Plausible Inference, Morgan Kaufmann Publishers Inc., San Mateo, California.

[22]Pearl, J. and Verma, T. (1987) The Logic of Representing Dependencies by Directed Graphs, Proceedings of AAAI-87, Volume 1, Sixth International Conference on Artificial Intelligence, Morgan Kaufmann Publishers Inc., California, pp. 374–379.

[23]Rybolt, W., Kopsco, D. and Pipino, L.L. (1990) Imputation of the Algorithms for Certainty Factor Manipulation by Individuals Using Neural Networks and Regression: A Comparison to Expert System Shells, Proceedings of the Twenty-Third Annual Hawaii International Conference on System Sciences, Volume IV, IEEE Computer Society Press, Los Alamitos, California, pp. 353–362.

[24]Schocken, S. and Kleindorfer, P. (1987) Artificial Intelligence Dialects of the Bayesian Belief Language, NYU Graduate School of Business Administration, working paper number 87-73.

[25]Simon, H.A. (1954) Spurious Correlations: A Causal Interpretation, Journal of the American Statistical Association, 49, 467-479; reprinted in [4].

[26]Simon, H.A., (1957) Models of Man, John Wiley & Sons Inc., New York.

[27]Smithson, M. (1989) Ignorance and Uncertainty: Emerging Paradigms, Springer-Verlag, New York.

[28]Spiegelhalter, D.J. (1986) A Statistical View of Uncertainty in Expert Systems, in [10].

[29]Wright, S. (1934) The Method of Path Coefficients, Annals of Mathematical Statistics, 5, pp. 161–215.

[30] Wright, S. (1960) The Treatment of Reciprocal Interaction, With or Without Lag, in Path Analysis, Biometrics, 16, pp. 423–455.

[31] Wright, S. (1988) Evolution and the Genetics of Populations, Volume 1: Genetic and Biometric Foundations, The University of Chicago Press, Chicago, Illinois.